CULTIVATING CUSTOMERS

CULTIVATING CUSTOMERS

A FARMER'S GUIDE TO ONLINE MARKETING

SIMON HUNTLEY

CULTIVATING CUSTOMERS
A Farmer's Guide to Online Marketing

ISBN   978-1-61961-471-0   *Paperback*
       978-1-61961-472-7   *Ebook*

INTERIOR DESIGN BY
www.DominiDragoone.com

LIONCREST
PUBLISHING

To all the Small Farm Central customers who have grown with me for the last 10 years, and to my wife and boys for keeping me grounded at home.

🖋🖋🖋

# CONTENTS

PART 3: SELLING YOUR WARES

 # FOREWORD

In my hometown of Goshen, Indiana, in the past four years, three big-box stores—Walmart, Aldi, and Target—dramatically increased their organic food lines. Another regional grocery chain put up a neighborhood store full of organic options just a few miles down the road from the farmers' market. Goshen is a town of just thirty thousand residents, but there are now dozens of places to buy naturally raised food.

These trends are national, and local farmers feel the impact. As Simon Huntley notes, the pace of farmers' market growth is slowing. On average, community-supported agricultures (CSAs) now lose at least 50 percent of their customers every year. Not long ago, CSAs and farmers' markets filled a niche. Now they are just two options in a sea of choices. The market window for small farms, it seems, is closing.

It's time to stop and rethink our marketing, which is why I read this book enthusiastically. It is chock full of ideas to combat this new competition and turn farmers into shrewd marketers.

Cultivating Customers is about taking seriously the job of selling. At Clay Bottom Farm, we've tried some ideas that Simon talks about in this book, and they work. A few years ago, we started to survey our CSA customers multiple times per season, asking what they might want more or less of. We use the information to structure our CSA each season. We ask how we might improve our service, too. The result: we installed refrigeration units at our CSA pickup locations so customers could pick up at their convenience. Eventually, we partnered with our food co-op as our primary pickup location; most of our customers shop there anyway, so the arrangement saves a trip.

In addition, we opened an Instagram account, beefed up our Facebook presence, redesigned our website with Squarespace, and started e-mail marketing with Small Farm Central and MailChimp. We now text-message our chefs twice a week.

We are doing basic marketing required to stay viable. This book goes deeper. Simon skillfully explains today's Internet-based marketing options. Farmers rely on tools to get jobs done. This book will show you a new set of tools that could quickly become among the most powerful on your farm.

Small farms have these key advantages: a story people want to hear and a human face behind food. "No one wants to hear the story of how their factory-farmed eggs are produced," Simon writes. By contrast, eaters everywhere, it seems, want to know their farmers and hear their trials and triumphs. They want authenticity. We can give that to them, but Walmart can't.

The idea behind this book isn't to get you out of the fields and behind the screen. It's to show you how to tell your story in the most efficient way possible, using the best tools available right now. Be selective. Don't use every social media platform ever invented. Pick a few that make the most sense in your context. Use efficient processes (on our farm, we normally spend less than twenty minutes per week on Internet marketing) so that you get your story out quickly between trellising tomatoes and seeding radishes. For sure, the Internet can be a rabbit hole, gobbling your time and money. That's why I read this book with a notepad in hand and came away with a to-do—and a stop-doing—list that I'm confident will cut out screen-time waste.

Market farmers, it's time to retool our marketing. Read on. Simon will show you how.

BEN HARTMAN
Clay Bottom Farm
Goshen, Indiana
Author of *The Lean Farm*

THE ONLINE BUSINESS OF FOOD

F armers don't mince words. They have no time to waste. They're knee-deep in the fields and chest-deep in chores, so I'll cut to the chase.

Small farms and farmers' markets, as well as local food businesses and community-supported agriculture (CSAs), are way behind the curve when it comes to marketing in the digital age.

There's been an amazing shift toward local food in the last decade. Yet the growth rate for farmers' markets and CSAs is slowing down. Overall dollars spent on local food is far more than it used to be, but the local-food pie is becoming more fragmented. The local farmer's slice is getting smaller because there's more competition.

Silicon Valley thinks there's something to this local food thing— and they're right. Startups and local-food funds are popping up all over the country. Some $6.8 billion is invested worldwide in food tech startups.

As every small farmer, CSA operator, and market stall vendor knows, the competition is growing stiffer. Customers have more and more options for buying locally sourced food. Whole Foods, online farmers' markets, food hubs, and even conventional grocery stores all want a piece of the pie.

In our interconnected world where food is just a click away, the old model of field to market is being challenged. Independent farmers and local food entrepreneurs need to expand their horizons through digital media. It's time to take the bull by the horns. So let me be blunt.

A farm without marketing is just a big compost pile.

The fact is that "agripreneurs" keep making the same mistakes. CSAs that deliver delicious boxes of fresh produce are going under because they can't find enough members. Farmers' markets are barely breaking even. Small farmers just aren't adequately cultivating the business side of growing. Meanwhile, the expanding local food movement is leaving farmers high and dry.

WANT TO MAKE A MILLION DOLLARS IN FARMING? START WITH TWO MILLION.

It's an old joke, one I've heard all my life working in and around farms. Invest in a small farm and you'll probably lose your overalls. But the old joke has gained new currency in these competitive times. A recent *Salon* article, "What Nobody Told Me About Small Farming: I Can't Make a Living," has gotten considerable play, along with *The New York Times* piece called, "Don't Let Your Children Grow Up to Be Farmers." It's an old story dressed up for a new age.

I was at a farming conference last year that offered hundreds of sessions on everything from small-scale hops growing to balancing farming with family life. However, not one session addressed the topic of farming profitably. How many attendees will still be able to afford to attend the conference next year?

It's time we had a frank discussion about the facts of farm life. Small farmers need to make money to ensure the long-term viability of their farms. Local food growers and farmers' markets need to tap viable markets and a widening customer base. It's the only way to survive and attract the kind of smart, ambitious young people who can make a go of the complex system that is the modern small farm.

I'm not talking about Wall Street-type profit-making. I'm talking about providing a valuable product to customers and getting fairly compensated. I'm talking about building small farms and local food businesses. It's not about getting rich. It's about having farms that work for families. It's about sustainability in the long term.

THE COMPETITIVE LANDSCAPE

We're at a crossroads where big food companies and startups are competing for the same food dollars that have been spent at farmers' markets and CSAs. We've reached a time when the local food movement must mature by making local food economically sustainable.

We need farms that reward farm families for their hard work and investment. It's no small thing to provide a family with a middle-class living. There are mortgages to pay, insurance, retirement savings, home improvements, and saving for education.

I grew up on a small farm in southwestern Pennsylvania in old sheep farming country. My parents raised livestock on 70 acres, of which only two or three were flat land. We grew hay and had a huge vegetable garden. But my folks never made a living from the farm. They worked off-farm jobs—my dad as a coal miner and my mom as a university professor.

My parents ran their farm as a sideline and I helped out, but I was always more interested in computers and programming than farming. I ended up attending Penn State, where I tinkered with technology, took agriculture classes, and volunteered on the campus farm. I was especially interested in the business side of agriculture, CSAs, and the local-food movement, probably because I'd grown up on a farm that wasn't profitable.

After school I moved to western Colorado where I helped a peach farmer start a CSA and gained hands-on experience in the business of farming. I came to see how agricultural sustainability goes hand-in-hand with economic sustainability. A question kept nagging me: Could I make a living at this long term?

I found myself looking at the business angle first and the romance of farming second. If a farm isn't a viable business, it doesn't make sense to me. I'm not idealistic about farming. I'm practical.

When I was home visiting my parents' farm recently, I spoke with one of my parent's friends, a farmer I've known all my life. He was lamenting the fact that none of the kids who grew up in the farm community still live there. He told me, "You all went urban." He'd hoped to be "an old sage" at his stage of life, teaching everything he'd learned over the years. His little farm community had declined, an experience mirrored all across the country. Fewer and fewer young people see farming as a viable profession.

GETTING PERSONAL AND DIGITAL

I know from experience that if we don't have strong farm businesses, we won't have full-time farmers. We won't have people who can really take care of their farms and the land. So I combined my technical and farming interests to develop software services to help farmers grow their businesses. I started Small Farm Central in 2006 to connect with professional farmers and to serve their need for a sustainable living. I basically went into business to help small farmers make money at what they do best.

The farming landscape has changed drastically since I started Small Farm Central 10 years ago: there are more customers than ever interested in local food, but there are also more choices than ever for them to purchase food they feel good about. The marketing opportunities have also changed: now there is Facebook and Twitter; email marketing has matured further, and with all of these opportunities comes confusion. How does a farmer put all of these pieces together into a coherent marketing strategy while still finding the time to grow food?

Cultivating Customers seeks to provide a common sense marketing approach that respects the fact that as a farmer, there are many chores to finish *after* marketing.

For example, at farmers' markets, there's great opportunity in turning occasional customers into weekly customers. These customers who come a few times a year can be engaged via a streamlined communication strategy and will become weekly customers over time. These are people who are "on the bubble." They don't just need locally sourced food; they need a good story to go with it.

By focusing on engagement and the "lifecycle" of the customer, local food producers are increasing their market share. We are raising interest in local food by establishing relationships with customers around fresh ingredients, great recipes, and eating well.

Through social media, we are reaching into the digital world and growing our customer base.

It's not all positive as the local food market matures. There will be winners and losers. In Pittsburgh where I live, a pioneering farmers' market recently shut down. They were the very first organic market in the city. What happened is the world caught up to their vision of organic and local food. In their closing email, they wrote that "the ubiquitous farmers' markets and availability of organic food in every store now has made it very difficult for us to keep going."

Food businesses from the local grocery store to specialty stores like Whole Foods and delivery services are eyeing our best farmers' market customers. They've raised their game and we need to raise ours to compete.

A "CALL TO ARMS"

In *Cultivating Customers*, I'll show you how to raise your game. As a marketer and a business person who wants to see more farmers succeed financially, this book is my call to arms.

Farmers' market organizers have multiple goals: fresh local food, community development, "placemaking," and creating public spaces. Yet the heart of the farmers' market is the farmer. And the continued viability of the market is the financial well-being of the farmer. It's fine to have weekend gardeners bringing produce to market, but hobby farmers aren't as invested in farm life as are professional growers.

Customers need economically vibrant vendors. A professional grower who can invest in a high tunnel to extend the tomato harvest can extend the season and keep the market open an extra month. She can invest in post-harvest cooling to keep her vegetables top notch. She has a wide array of products for sale. This is the kind of farmer who can also extend her marketing. She can invest in signage, digital outreach, and well-trained and friendly staff.

We all know farmers like this. There is one at our farmers' market in the up-and-coming East Liberty neighborhood in Pittsburgh. This farmer has 20 or 30 customers in line and a staff of four or five keeping them happy. The products look great, the signage is great, and the staff are wearing matching shirts and smiling and having fun.

People are willing to wait for the experience of buying from this farmer. Farmers who are making a good living are a draw for long-term customers. It's the beauty of direct marketing—talking to the customer, establishing and sustaining relationships. In these digital times, people are finding community online.

THE STORY SELLS

Our competition are companies like Good Eggs backed by $52 million in venture capital, delivering farm-fresh groceries to the customer's door. But they've got nothing genuinely personal to sell. The competition is Blue Apron delivering ready-made, perfectly apportioned meals. But nothing personal. Small farmers, CSAs, and farmers' markets can compete with better product, sustained personalized marketing, and the human touch.

As Farmer John of Angelic Organics near Chicago says, *"The relationship needs to be with the farm and not just the food."*

The food that the customer brings home from a farmers' market is infused with the experience of buying from the source, supporting local farms, and a good, warm feeling about the quality of their purchase. Good food is easy to find in many places now, but food with a story is special. Large corporations and startups can't compete on the personal level.

In *Cultivating Customers,* you'll see how to bring that personal touch to marketing using digital tools.

I've been heard to say that farmers' markets are a bad business model. What I mean by this is: Can you name another business model that operates only half the year for three or four hours a week?

It's hard for customers to get used to a schedule like that. Once they do, the market shuts down for six months, and they have to go elsewhere. Even in season, farmers' markets require strong customer commitment—an extra shopping trip in already crowded schedules. Yet there are more than 9,000 farmers' markets in the United States. So there's clearly something compelling about them that keeps customers coming back.

Customers at farmers' markets and CSAs are willing to invest their time and hard-earned cash in exceptional product and a unique story. Which is why small farmers and vendors need to tell the story of their farms, their vision and place in the community, local environment, and the economy. We need to connect the dots of why local food is important for health and well-being. We can't simply trust that our customers know. We need to keep sharing our stories so customers get to know us.

And that campfire today includes Twitter and Snapchat, Facebook and YouTube. Customers need to see both the individual and the larger context. It bears repeating year after year as you bring more people into your orbit. Let them know about your product and you the grower, your livestock, your farm culture, and family. Customers are our extended family. They're partners in our cause. They share our passions for quality food and healthy eating.

The Facebook page of Scenic Pastures Farm in Fall Creek, Wisconsin is a place for potential customers and regular customers to connect with the farm. They celebrate their customers on "CSA Day" by giving away a "farm bundle" of farm-raised meat, homemade salve, and a $10 gift certificate. They post a video of the drawing for the winner.

The Western Wake Farmers' Market alerts customers via text message. If the weather is bad, they'll text, "Hey, it's raining, but we're still open. We'll see you there!"

In *Cultivating Customers,* you'll find many such strategies, from customer rewards to VIP cookouts. You'll learn about:

- Customer retention
- Marketing plans
- Key performance indicators
- Tracking your metrics
- Social media followers
- Email lists
- Website visits
- Setting year-to-year goals
- Month-by-month planning
- Your perfect customer profile

This book is structured in three parts and is easy to follow.

Part 1 presents a marketing philosophy and framework that has worked for hundreds of local food businesses. You'll become acquainted with an overall digital strategy for marketing your business and *Cultivating Customers.*

Part 2 presents more specific strategies and tactics for each digital marketing channel, including social media, website, email, and more.

Part 3 presents marketing techniques for specific venues, such as farmers' markets, CSAs, and restaurants.

There are challenges ahead for the local-food community, but I've seen how people who can work a farm can work the Internet. Online marketing is a whole lot easier and requires much less time than working a farm.

Digital media are just another farm tool.

So let's dig in and start *Cultivating Customers*.

PART 1:
DIGITAL MARKETING

CHAPTER 1
YOUR IDEAL CUSTOMER

I magine a traditional bakery advertising in a gluten-free newsletter. Pretty ridiculous, right? When you're selling food, it's tempting to think, "Well, everyone eats, so everyone is my customer!" That might seem true, but it isn't, at least not from a marketing point of view.

If you want to see results from your marketing efforts, you need to focus your time and resources on specific segments of customers. You need to target your most likely buyers.

A grower of microgreens has a very different market than a sweet-corn vendor. However, a farmers' market manager would want to have both stalls open on a Saturday afternoon.

The key to marketing local food is to understand:
1. *Who* are your customers?
2. *How* do you reach them?
3. *Where* do you reach them?

FINDING YOUR CUSTOMER

Local farmers have several venues for finding customers. At the top of the list are farmers' markets and CSAs. When it comes to farmers' markets, there are three main groups of shoppers:

- **The Faithful Shopper** (comes every week and spends $50)
- **The Occasional Shopper** (comes three or four times a year)
- **The Day Tripper** (comes once a year)

Of course, every person is unique. Within each of these groups there are individuals with their own tastes and habits. Everyone has their own motivations for where and when they shop.

So let's break things down a little further.

YOUR IDEAL CUSTOMER

I use the expression *customer persona* to describe a particular kind of customer—your *ideal* customer. As you'll see, the ideal customer model is applicable and adaptable to both farmers' markets and CSAs.

Your ideal customer is a real person. She has a name. He has hopes and dreams. Try to imagine your ideal customer.

Ask yourself these questions.
- What is the customer's name, gender, and age?
- Does your customer persona have children? How many? Ages?
- Where does she live?
- Where does he work?
- Does she belong to any community organizations?
- How often does she shop at a farmers' market?

- What else is vying for her attention on the days when the market is open?
- How much does he spend on food?
- Where else does he buy food?
- Why does he come to the market?
- What would make her skip coming to the market?
- How price conscious is she?
- How often does he cook?

If you are a market manager:
- What stands does she shop at?

When brainstorming customer personas for your business, it's best to focus on the Occasional Shopper. If you can get her to the market twice as often, and she spends 20% more each time, it's a huge win for your stand (if you're a farmer) or your market as a whole (if you're the market manager).

So let's take a look at the math. If she visited four times last year and spent $20 each time, her total was $80. If you can get her to visit eight times and spend $24 each time, she'll be spending $112 more. So it's worth focusing on your Occasional Shopper. Bring her around as a Faithful Shopper.

Keep these facts in mind:
- Your Faithful Shopper is already a super fan, a true believer.
- The Occasional Shopper is your fence sitter. Your job is to get her off the fence and on your side. She's your target customer.
- It's much harder to convince a Day Tripper to become a Faithful Shopper.

If you have a team working in your business, it's a good idea to ask everyone to create a persona on their own. Then bring everyone together to compare. It's a great way to create an accurate picture of your ideal customer.

Your goal is to build out a complete persona. Who are they? What are they like? What do they care about? What gets them fired up? If you do this right, you'll start to think of them as a real person. Take Jill, for instance.

JILL: A CUSTOMER PERSONA

Jill is 34, a nurse with one young child. She lives about a mile from the farmers' market. She attends a local church and most of her free time is spent with her family and child-centered activities. She comes to the Saturday market about once a month, when she remembers to.

She isn't faithful to any one stand. She walks around and buys what looks good. She fills in the gaps by shopping at a grocery store later in the week. Jill has been part of a CSA before, but found that it required too much commitment. She prefers the social experience of the farmers' market.

Jill spends about $30 at the market divided among two vegetable growers, one baker, and some prepared food to take home for dinner.

She's a supporter of local food because she believes it's an important environmental issue but mainly because the food tastes better. Also, the whole experience makes her feel better than shopping at the grocery store. She feels that her spending supports local businesses and keeps farmers on their land. Home cooking and food are important to her. She cooks five to seven days a week, but feels rushed in the kitchen. She's always looking for new cooking ideas.

GET TO KNOW YOUR CUSTOMERS

After you've come up with your first customer persona, it's time to test it in the field.

You've already spent a lot of time with customers at the market. Now it's time to watch them with the keen eye of an anthropologist. For the sake of learning, try to forget your first impressions. Try to see your customers again in a new light. A beginner's mind. You want to glean new insights. You want to see what you may have overlooked in the past.

At the farmers' market, don't just sell, talk. Engage your customers. Feel them out. What do they like to eat? What are they looking for? Have you seen them before? How often do they come?

THE CUSTOMER SURVEY

It isn't difficult to put together a one-page survey to get to know your customers better. You can hand surveys out at your stand or via an email list. It's all part of reaching out. Let your customers know you want to stay in touch. You goal is to build a sense of community. You want to extend a feeling of belonging and sharing of common goals.

You want customers to know that you want to serve them better.

SURVEY QUESTIONS TO ASK YOUR CUSTOMERS

- How did you first learn about our farm or food business?
- What is most important to you about buying local food?
- How comfortable do you feel in the kitchen?
- How often do you buy from us?
- What would encourage you to shop with us more?
- Are there any products we don't offer that you'd like us to?
- What is the biggest impediment to buying from us?
- How would you like to stay in touch? Email? Social network? Phone?

The last question is extremely important. Surveys help establish lines of communication: Facebook friends, email addresses, and phone numbers. Direct calls to customers are especially powerful in the off-season. You can put a recurring reminder on your calendar to start calling around December 1.

When you have a customer on the phone, try to help them feel comfortable. Let them know who you are. Remind them that you need honest feedback—all the good, the bad, and the ugly. Let them lead the conversation. Give them the space to elaborate. You want to know their insights.

If a customer says they "don't have enough time" to visit the market regularly, try to look deeper. What other commitments are they balancing? How can you help make the market more relevant, a bigger priority in their lives? Be patient and listen, always.

The more you get to know your individual customers, the more you'll know how to tailor your business to their needs. Remember: Marketing is all about filling a need.

CHAPTER 2
BUILDING ONLINE INTEREST

Now that you know who your target customers are, let's dig deeper into how to generate customer interest using online tools.

Your story is your most powerful marketing asset. And one of the best ways to get your story out is through social media.

SOCIAL PLATFORMS

The local food movement is highly visual. Fields of greens, colorful fruits and vegetables, brimming farm stands, and farm scenes are pleasing to behold. Social media platforms that highlight visual media work best to carry your online message. Platforms like Facebook, Instagram, and to a lesser extent, Pinterest, are great ways to share your story online.

Rather than trying to spread yourself too thin, start with one or two platforms and expand from there when you're ready.

Building a fan page on Facebook is an opportunity to communicate your business and connect with existing and potential customers. The best way to get started on Facebook is to simply commit to sharing your story. You'll naturally connect with your existing followers and grow as you go.

Instagram is dominated by photos and is therefore tailor-made for food growers and marketers. Many of the farmers I've worked with have had great success with Instagram. It's a "no-brainer" addition to your marketing plan.

We'll go more deeply into the nuts and bolts of social media in Chapter 6.

EMAIL MARKETING

Marketing by email is an often-overlooked strategy, simply because it's not as trendy as some of the newer platforms. But it's still one of the most effective communication tools for local food businesses. If you can communicate effectively to your customers via email, you're tapping into a one-to-one messaging platform that is as old as the Internet itself. And despite what many people say about the demise of email, most of us are still paying attention to our inboxes.

There are, however, some big mistakes to be made in email marketing, which I'll cover in Chapter 8. For now, simply setting up an email list is a good start. There are plenty of free marketing solutions for managing email and tracking results, such as MailChimp.

If you don't already have a website or blog, it's time you did. Websites and blogs are easier to put together and maintain than ever before. They also don't cost much to run. You don't even have to hire a website developer or designer. You can find a wealth of do-it-yourself information online. There are plenty of how-to videos on YouTube.

You can purchase your website name (called a domain or URL) from registrars such as GoDaddy and set up your own website using ready-made templates from WordPress. Easy website hosting can be found at HostGator, Bluehost, and many others. If you're already using email through Google, you can set up a blog through your Gmail account.

I actually started Small Farm Central back in 2006 to help local farmers build websites. Farmers had been telling me they didn't have the time or know-how to do it themselves and it was way too costly to hire a web developer. So I began working on solutions for farm-friendly websites that would work well for local farms with limited budgets and time. We found a way to build customizable templates designed to meet the particular needs of small farms and we created a support system and hosting geared specifically to local farmers. Our Site Builder tool is still an important part of what we do at Small Farm Central, along with other e-commerce tools.

We'll discuss websites in greater detail in Chapter 7.

ONLINE ADS

One of the easiest ways to get started with online advertising is through Google AdWords and Facebook. I've experimented with other platforms, but I find these are still miles ahead of most other options.

It's essential to target your advertising geographically and by specific interest in order to maximize results. With Facebook, you can target ads to people with interests such as locally sourced food, CSAs, or farmers' markets to better reach your customer personas.

With any online paid advertising, it's important to track performance. You can do so by offering a coupon or other incentive that brings customers to your market stall, or to sign up for your CSA. In this way, you can gauge response. Knowing your results is extremely important when it comes to paid traffic through ads. It's too easy to spend money quickly with paid advertising. So be sure to measure your results.

You can set any budget you like to make sure that your daily ad spending doesn't get out of control. On some platforms it's possible to spend as little as $5/day. There's room for testing and experimenting, then scaling up as you see positive results.

Many strategies work. I've seen farms and markets achieve success by simply "boosting" posts on their Facebook pages. It's a good, low-cost place to start and see how it works out for your business. You can get more advanced results by re-targeting your website visitors. Well-planned strategies can justify the investment of time and money. You'll find out more on boosting posts in Chapter 6.

SEARCH ENGINE OPTIMIZATION

Search Engine Optimization (SEO) involves using keywords in your website pages that match what potential customers are searching. If you run a farmers' market in Lexington, Virginia, you'd certainly want to embed the words "farmers' market" and

"Lexington, Virginia" while you're at it. Most local food businesses do very well by simply optimizing three to five quality keywords.

You don't have to hire an SEO consultant to attain excellent results. You can work some basic SEO tasks into your weekly marketing schedule. In Chapter 10, we'll take a more extensive look at how to approach SEO.

CASE STUDY: EARLY MORNING FARM

If this is the first time you're diving deep into online marketing, it may feel somewhat overwhelming. I suggest exploring how other farms promote themselves online.

Let's take a look now at how my friend Anton Burkett markets his operation. Anton runs Early Morning Farm, one of the largest and most successful CSA farms in the Northeast. The farm began in 1999 with just three acres of land, three friends, and one garden-sized rototiller.

Early Morning Farm has done an exceptional job of building online interest. Their email marketing, social media, website, and search engine optimization are all superb.

In social media, they focus on Facebook, Pinterest, Instagram, and Twitter. Facebook is their primary focus. Right from the start they began using Facebook fan pages to promote their business and build a thriving community. Here's how they use their cover image (*following page*).

It's a shot of their farm in the background with a call-to-action to sign up for a CSA share and save money. This is just about the

only direct advertising they do on their page. Everything else they post is either a delicious recipe shared from their website or a picture with some news from the farm. They're providing a ton of value to their fans and CSA members, while also continually advertising their farm right up at the top. It's a textbook case of using Facebook effectively.

Facebook is Early Morning Farm's main social media channel. But they use other channels as well, including Twitter, Pinterest, and Instagram. Although they have fewer followers and engagement on those platforms, they are regularly updated. All are business drivers.

Early Morning Farm's website is another business driver. When you go the homepage, you're presented with the following:

- Options for buying a CSA share
- Areas they serve
- A link to their blog for recipes, harvest updates, and news
- A link to what's inside a typical CSA box
- Their pickup locations

THE EARLY MORNING FARM STAFF

JOIN OUR CSA

PICK-UP LOCATIONS

SHARE OPTIONS

RECIPES

Everything you see is with a purpose. Anton knows exactly what people are looking for when they consider investing in a CSA share. It's all there right on the farm's website homepage. Visitors can find everything they need to know, no matter how new they are to CSAs.

A homepage or landing page is just the first page of a website, and arguably the most important. As you've already learned, your story is the most important asset you have when it comes to marketing. Early Morning Farm does a fantastic job of telling their story.

On other pages they present their mission: To Grow Fresh, Organic Food and Strengthen Our Local Community of Eaters.

They tell you their value: Community, Accessibility, Sustainability.

They even have a personalized bio page introducing everyone who works on the farm (*previous page*). Notice the sidebar in this image. It contains links to every important page on their site:

- How to join their CSA
- Where to pick up a share
- Types of shares you can purchase
- Recipes

It's a beautiful presentation of every stage of the CSA buying process, from research to retention. We'll get deeper into the intricacies of CSAs in Chapter 14.

They provide an easy signup for their email newsletter in which they share news from the farm, recipes, and promotions. At the time of this book's publication, they were promoting *National CSA Sign-Up Day* with a $25-off promo code, asking their subscribers to "invest in your local food system!"

Early Morning Farm does a great job of weaving in messaging that resonates with their target customer, while providing incentives to pull the trigger on a CSA share.

Take a look at their website, their social media, and email marketing for yourself. Search other local farms that are doing the same. There are great examples out there to aspire to. Take some time and poke around and ask yourself, "What can I learn from what they are doing and how can I apply it to my own operation?"

CHAPTER 3
THE CUSTOMER LIFECYCLE

You've developed your customer personas. You have an overview of options for getting the word out online. It's time now to understand your customer's lifecycle.

THE MARKETING FUNNEL

From the first time a customer hears about you to the moment he visits your stall, market, or CSA and makes a purchase, he is in your "marketing funnel."

It's called a funnel because everyone starts at the top in the broadest part of the funnel. This is the "awareness" phase of the customer lifecycle. During this phase, customers are interested, if not in you directly, then in the idea of a CSA share, shopping at a farmers' market, or in simply buying local food. It's a beginning. Perhaps they've come to know about your local food business. Perhaps they've gained this awareness and interest through some of the online marketing strategies you've applied.

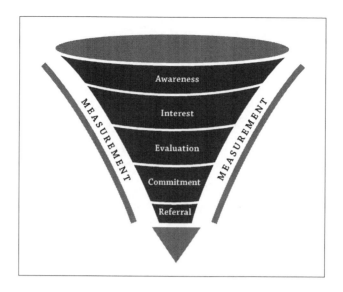

THE AWARENESS PHASE

The awareness phase is a good beginning. But if there's no movement down the funnel, if there's no action, not much will happen.

Some people at the top won't go any further. They'll slip out of your funnel before they get started. They'll never actually come to the farmers' market to meet you and make a purchase.

There's a big gap between getting a potential customer interested and getting them to make a purchase. In my work with local growers and markets I stress the importance of bridging that gap.

It's not enough for someone to "like" your farm's post on Facebook. It's a start, but your employees don't get paid in Facebook likes. We need to learn how to get an online follower to come to market, make a purchase, and show support for local food businesses.

We need them to enter the next phase through the funnel. We need to capture their awareness and turn a potential customer into a real-life customer.

Movement down the funnel begins in the "evaluation" phase of the customer lifecycle.

The marketing funnel depicts the journey.

THE EVALUATION PHASE

So you've gained a customer's interest through social media, your website, email, advertising, or word of mouth. Your potential customers know you exist. They are aware of you. Give yourself a good pat on the back. However, you're just beginning.

Unfortunately, many farms don't understand how to lead people from awareness and interest to the evaluation phase.

Before we look at how to bridge this gap, let's understand what's happening in the evaluation phase. Your potential customer may be able to name a few of the local farms or farmers' markets, but she doesn't yet have an affinity for a particular local food business.

She hasn't yet evaluated the options that exist.

In this phase, the strength of your brand really matters. Because we're all bombarded by so many marketing messages throughout our days and lives, we typically focus on the few companies that break through the noise. In local food, this means that markets with the most visibility and farms that do the best job of telling their story garner the most attention.

In the local food industry, customers tend to be conscious and engaged. When people decide to look into local food, they really look. You therefore need to do everything in your power to provide potential customers with the information they need to make a decision and commit to your business.

THE IMPORTANCE OF CAPTURE IN THE EVALUATION PHASE

When an aware customer visits your website or finds you on social media, it's important to establish an ongoing connection. You need to "capture" their contact information to begin the conversation. The two primary pieces of contact information are:

1. Email address
2. Cell phone number for text-message marketing

Social media is a great tool, but the engagement rates on social media are disturbingly low. Social media works best in the awareness phase of the funnel when a potential customer has "liked" you and is "following" you. But many of these folks aren't ready to start the journey through the funnel. They won't become customers unless we proactively move them down the funnel.

Capture contact information by offering a "carrot," by which I don't mean the root vegetable. I mean something attractive and inviting. An incentive. Try to go beyond "Join Our Mailing List," by offering something of value. Share recipes. Bring them to market with a discount coupon offer, a weekly special, or a loyalty program. When you give folks a good reason to provide their email addresses or cell phone numbers, you'll have a much higher opt-in rate.

When you have one or two pieces of contact information, you can go beyond Facebook. You can go directly to your potential customers. Offer them the kind of information and incentives to help them through the evaluation phase to the commitment phase of the funnel.

THE COMMITMENT PHASE

Congratulations, you've successfully guided a potential customer through the evaluation phase to the next phase in the journey. They are moving through the marketing funnel to a place where they can make a purchase with you.

However, there's still some distance to travel in the customer lifecycle. It's a whole lot easier to keep an existing customer than to create a new one.

In the commitment phase, fostering repeat sales is your main focus. How can you get them back to the market week after week? How can you make sure they sign up for your CSA next year?

In the following pages you'll find out how to deepen your customer relationships and retain committed customers for the long term.

ACTION PLAN

Review each phase of the marketing funnel and customer lifecycle and jot down a few notes.

Keep these definitions in mind:
* *Awareness*: Potential customer hears about your farm, farmers' market, or local food business.

- *Interest*: Potential customer "likes" you on Facebook or visits your website.
- *Evaluation*: Potential customer joins your email list or visits the market.
- *Commitment*: Potential customer joins your loyalty program, becomes a regular customer, or joins your CSA.
- *Referral*: Encourage customers to tell their friends about your farm or market.
- *Repeat*: Encourage repeat customers.

CHAPTER 4
KEEP THEM COMING BACK

One of the biggest challenges with farmers' markets is to get repeat sales week after week. The occasional shopper who comes two or four times a season doesn't spend a whole lot of money. It's a huge win to get a customer to double their shopping or spend even 25% more.

The questions we need to ask ourselves are:

- How can I make it as easy as possible for someone to buy from me?
- How can I keep them coming back?

There are many creative ways to go about it. And it all starts with communication.

TIMING YOUR COMMUNICATIONS

It's important to send an email to customers 24 hours before market day. You want to build excitement. Let them know it's the first week of strawberry season in your subject line:

"TOMORROW! Come get the first local, ripe strawberries of the season!"

Use your email marketing tool's statistics on open and click rates to gauge subject lines that work.

If you're using text messaging with our FarmFan app or another platform, your message should be perfectly timed.

- For weekday markets, it should go out about two hours before the market starts.
- For weekend morning markets, the sweet spot is 9 a.m.

Emails, social media, and text message updates should all be scheduled ahead of time. Keep to a workable schedule so online marketing doesn't interfere with the work of growing and bringing food to market.

Effective and timely communications help build your customer base and your brand. You're striving to grow well-informed, regular, and loyal customers.

YOUR COMMUNICATION SYSTEM

An organized communication process that reaches the most people each market week will maximize your chance of repeat sales.

Market season is a busy time for farmers, vendors, and market managers alike. So it's important to build a marketing system in advance. During the off-season, develop a set of steps that can be executed efficiently when market season opens.

I recommend that you plan for two separate pieces of communication each week.

The first is for brand building. In this communication you share your story. You describe your farm. You introduce your operation, family, and staff. You personalize the work you do. You share your mission and goals. Potential customers have many options for food buying, so make the case for why they should buy from you. Share photos of your farm, the work of growing, and the relationships that make your farm function smoothly.

In the second piece of communication focus on generating excitement about the upcoming market each week. What produce will you be bringing to sell? Offer incentives and special offers, those "carrots" we discussed in Chapter 3.

Use your online marketing tools:
- Blog on your website.
- Send market-specific communications by email.
- Provide updates on Facebook.
- Send informative Twitter tweets several times a week using a scheduling tool.
- Photo-share and video-share on Instagram.

To get measurable data about the success of your posts, use Facebook Page Insights or Twitter analytics. Note the number of views and clicks you get with each of your posts. Refine your messaging to increase the engagement rate.

PROVIDE RECIPES

Providing recipes online or at the point of sale is a great way to engage customers. It provides context for the food you sell. People always want to know how to bring more variety to their cooking. Preparing and eating good food builds relationships, community, and customer loyalty.

A CSA box of raw produce can be intimidating. People want to know how to use it and enjoy it. It takes skill and practice to combine ingredients for a family-pleasing meal. You can widen your reach and your sales by educating customers about how best to prepare the food you sell.

People love recipes because it takes the stress out of cooking. Recipes also help to increase sales for those less common items you grow.

MARKET CARDS

Prepaid market cards are a fantastic way for farmers' market vendors to increase return visits. These cards usually include a discount for buying ahead of time. Customers love to get value on their dollar. So give them what they want. Help them save. Offer them more for their money and keep them coming back to your stand. Vendors track their prepaid sales and then transfer them to a spreadsheet later. This model is sometimes called a "market CSA."

GRATITUDE IS FREE

Remember: "Gratitude is free." This is especially true in the local food business. Making your customers feel valued pays huge dividends for you and your business.

People want to feel good about buying at farmers' markets. They are going out of their way to shop with you. So make sure they know how important their patronage is to your livelihood. This is something you can emphasize in emails and social media posts.

DEVELOP YOUR "FARM FANS"

Your model customer persona is one who's committed to seasonal, farm-fresh produce. She wants to feel connected to both the food and the grower.

For some customers, farmers' markets are the preferred way to support local farmers, because they don't want to be locked in with a CSA for the entire season. Maybe they travel too much, or they don't want their box packed for them. Or they just like the social aspect of farmers' markets.

As a farmer or market operator, it's part of your job to make every customer feel valued. In one study, it was shown that 68% of customers leave a business due to "perceived indifference." In other words, they didn't feel valued.

Loyalty programs can be thought of as a trade between you and your customers. You provide special offers and they give you permission to contact them. Effective loyalty programs go hand-in-hand with customer communication.

A simple rewards program is easy to run. All it requires is an email list or text-message distribution offering a special deal of the week. Only customers on your list get the deal, so there's an exclusivity to it. An appreciation factor is built in. It makes people feel special.

Many market managers struggle to get and retain good farmers and vendors. As a farmers' market manager, you can feature a different vendor each week in your specials message. It's a great way to drive traffic through the market. It builds good will among customers and vendors as well.

If you start your own rewards program, give it a name. The rewards program at Ferry Plaza Farmers' Market in San Francisco is called Seasonal Shopper Card. Another name I like is Rolling Hills Frequent Shoppers.

Create a logo for your rewards program that appears on your website. You can have a logo created at sites such as 99designs. A recognizable logo or mascot primes your customers.

We've developed an app called FarmFan to help farmers and market managers build stronger networks of supporters. Each week customers check in by text message and accumulate points that can be redeemed for rewards. The app sends updates to let customers know what their favorite vendors are bringing to market. It helps turn occasional shoppers into regulars.

Customers sign up for FarmFan by text, through social media, or on participating farm websites. The app provides a market check-in feature, a digital rewards punch card, and a loyalty program. It's a way to recognize customers and make them feel special. It helps market managers bring customers to market by generating a following. It provides reminders to CSA members on drop-off day. Customers get to call themselves "FarmFans," and we call them that too. It builds a local food identity.

One farmers' market manager I know had struggled with low morale and slumping sales. After introducing FarmFan at her markets, she had more than 100 customer signups in the first week. Her vendors were invigorated and she was looking forward to an exciting season of market sales.

The point is to help your customers feel connected. Let them know just how important their business is to you, your family, and your continued success.

TRACKING REWARDS

If you decide to run a farmers' market–wide rewards program, you'll need to approach it the right way. Excessive rewards can lose money.

Tracking customer spending through points—such as $1 = 1 point and 200 points gets a jar of jam—adds time and complexity to your program. This kind of tracking can be difficult to implement. How would you track $75 spent over six stalls by one customer?

It's much easier to track "check-ins." Each time someone comes to the market, he gets one check-in. After a certain number of check-ins, he gets a reward.

Farmers' markets that use our FarmFan app have a passcode for each market day that is distributed by vendors or market managers. The passcode is texted to FarmFan by the customer who receives a credit for his check-in. No work is required by vendors or market managers beyond giving out the passcode.

It builds enthusiasm all around. For customers it's an added bonus. It makes coming to the market a bit of a game.

You can learn more about FarmFan at http://about.farmfanapp.com

REWARDS

There are four different types of rewards you can offer to your customers, each with their own positives and negatives. Choose your rewards carefully, making sure to match them with what customers value most in your particular market or stall.

Monetary Rewards: The most obvious approach for rewards is to give people a deal for coming to the market throughout the season. For example, offering $5 off your next order for every five market check-ins.

A common mistake with monetary rewards is making them too generous. You can evaporate your profits quickly, so start low and increase if you like. It's much easier to increase than decrease them.

Swag Rewards: Printed bags, shirts, hats, or aprons with your farm or market logo are great reward program items. Customers won't often buy these products directly, but they enjoy them as rewards, especially if they like your farm or market.

With swag rewards, you're not only saying, "thank you" to your customer, you're also turning them into a walking advocate for your business!

Product-Centric Rewards: If you have a farm, there are times of the year when you have more tomatoes or greens than you can sell. A time-limited reward of canning tomatoes or an extra bunch of greens is a perfect solution. It's a great way to feature a product and help customers feel rewarded.

If you have a new value-added product like jam that is just coming to market, or a particular cut of meat that is lesser-known and doesn't normally sell, a product-centric reward is a fantastic way to feature the product and talk about it.

Experience-Based Rewards: The most creative FarmFan rewards programs are experience-based. These have included:

- A VIP farm tour and end-of-season cookout for customers who check in 10 times.
- A backyard garden consultation for 15 check-ins.
- An equipment tour of the farm for families with young children, for 20 check-ins.

Experience-based rewards are limited only by your creativity. They are an excellent way to make customers feel valued and excited when they shop with you. Every time they check in, they're making real progress toward a future experience they'll long remember.

These are also great ways to get to know your customers. You learn about where they come from, who they are, and what motivates them to come to market every week. There are multiple benefits from experience-based rewards, from customer appreciation to gaining valuable market research that can improve your marketing efforts.

A SAMPLE REWARDS PROGRAM

Kirsten Bansen Weigle, manager of the Maple Grove Farmers' Market in Minnesota, shares this experience of a simple, manually tracked rewards program:

"Our market offers a very simple loyalty punch card program. No purchase is necessary. Market guests stop by our information booth to complete a card. It's kept in a card file at the market. Each time they visit, they can stop by to receive a punch in the card. The first 250 customers to fill the card over the course of our 20-week season receive a $5 market token.

The loyalty card has generated a lot of good will and gives people a reason to stop by our info booth to say hi, ask questions, pick up free recipes, and swipe their credit cards. We think that over five years it has really fostered a sense of ownership in our market. We're a 45-vendor market most weeks, attracting an average of 2,000 adult shoppers, and we didn't quite make it to 250 completed cards this year. The punches are managed by a couple of our senior volunteers who find it very manageable."

CHAPTER 5
YOUR MARKETING PLAN

L et's take stock of what you've already learned.

* How to define your perfect farmers' market customer.
* The ways you can build interest in your farm or market online.
* How to close the gap between interest and sales.
* How to bring customers back for repeat sales.
* How to implement a loyalty or rewards program.

Where it all comes together is in your marketing plan. You'll be mapping out a process for achieving your goals for the upcoming season. At the end of the season you'll be able to look back and see if you met your goals.

By making your goals concrete, you're making them measurable. You'll be able to figure out how well you're doing, and how to adapt and improve.

KEY PERFORMANCE INDICATORS

Your marketing plan will include a section for Key Performance Indicators (KPIs). You'll pick key "metrics," which are factors you measure year-to-year to determine the success of your outreach efforts.

KPIs can include:

- Foot traffic at the farmers' market. (An important metric for market managers, although difficult to measure.)
- Email list growth. (An important metric for both farmers' markets and farms. I like this one because it's both easy to track and a reliable measure of your captive customer base.)
- Growth of your FarmFan list.
- Number of social media followers.
- Website traffic. (This is easy to measure, but I don't like it much because it doesn't necessarily translate into sales.)

You don't have to start your marketing plan just yet. Just keep it in mind as you read through the book.

In Part 2 we'll go deeper into online marketing tactics for social media, text messaging, websites, garnering reviews, customer retention, and so much more.

When you've reached the end of the book, you'll be ready to work on your marketing plan. In the appendix you'll find an easy-to-use marketing plan worksheet you can experiment with and customize for your own digital marketing needs.

PART 2:
STRATEGIES AND TACTICS

CHAPTER 6
SOCIAL MEDIA

Social media offers many opportunities for marketing farms, farmers' markets, and local food businesses. Although most farms already have social media presence, they don't optimize that presence. They write long blog posts that no one ends up reading.

In today's competitive social media culture, you must be hyper-aware of how and where people pay attention online. Otherwise your social media efforts will be wasted.

Here's a good example of a simple social media system that works well in today's environment:

• Facebook post on Monday morning.
• Email on Monday afternoon.
• Three tweets throughout the week.

This basic system can be made more complex over time. It's best to start small and post less often on fewer platforms. Once you start getting results, you can either adjust the type of content or the platforms you post on. The biggest trap is over-sharing and splitting focus.

The farms and farmers' markets that do well on social media all have one thing in common: The people who run these businesses really enjoy the social media side of the business.

These are the people who are posting to Facebook from their tractor or taking a picture of their fields for their Instagram account while they're out working.

Every social media tool has a different psychology and appeal. It's important to respect the platform. For example, Pinterest is highly visible, highly visual. Its main demographic is women age 25 to 54.

The one-to-one interaction with your fans on Twitter is second to none. If you're someone who's already on these platforms in your personal life, think about scaling up your activity and focusing on your farm business.

FACEBOOK STRATEGY

We covered the basics of Facebook in Chapter 2 when we looked at Early Morning Farm, but it's worth diving deeper into how to use Facebook for your local food business. The bottom line is this: If you had to pick only one social media platform to use, pick Facebook.

As of this writing in 2016, Facebook has 1.5 billion users, which is a truly amazing number. Facebook's reach is unparalleled by other platforms. Of the farmers I've worked with who've had the most success with social media, 95% of them concentrate on Facebook.

HOW FACEBOOK WORKS

Facebook's goal is to maximize the engagement of their users with the content in their feed. The platform uses algorithms to build each person's feed based on their past activity and the engagement rate of their posts. The more engagement your posts receive, such as likes and comments, the more likely it is they'll be shown to more people. In this way Facebook encourages users to create content that engages the Facebook audience. If you create engaging content, it's a win-win for both your market and Facebook.

The Facebook stats platform, Facebook Insights, is built into your page. Take a look at what you have posted recently. What got the most "reach?" For example, a reach of 1,000 would mean that 1,000 people saw the post on their feed.

On Facebook, you can:
- Share stories, images, recipes, and promotions via your page feed.
- Ask your customers to leave reviews (covered in depth in Chapter 11).
- Organize your photos into albums (similar to Pinterest).
- Give your customers all of the relevant information about your business.
- Link other platforms to Facebook, including getting email newsletter signups.

It can be a bit overwhelming to figure out what to do first. Let's take a look at an example of a farm that does an amazing job on Facebook.

A FARM ON FACEBOOK

Suzie's Farm in San Diego is a powerhouse. They sell produce in local grocery stores and farmers' markets, have their own CSA, and run workshops and tours on their farm.

Facebook is a core component of their marketing strategy. They have 310 reviews on Facebook with an average of 4.6/5 stars. Where most farms make Yelp or Google My Business their main review platform, Suzie's focuses on reviews on Facebook.

If you look at their Yelp profile, they have 48 reviews, just one-sixth of their Facebook reviews. Because they focus so heavily on Facebook as a communication platform, stacking all of their reviews on Facebook allows potential customers to see *exactly* how much they're loved in the community.

Their content is a mix of the following:
• Life on the farm
• Upcoming events and farmhouse dinners
• Recipes
• Contents of their CSA box

The key here is the mix. Most of their posts are helpful and interesting to their followers: recipes, CSA box contents (a great example of selling by showing), and life on the farm. Every now and then, they pepper in a post or two about upcoming events or make a harder promotional post about their CSA shares or farmers' market appearances.

By focusing more on how to deliver interesting, valuable content to their audience, they actually end up selling *more* CSA shares, getting *more* people out to their events, and getting *more* foot traffic at the market.

Here's their Facebook cover image (above). You'll see a button that says "Book Now." This is one of the more interesting strategies I've seen. Instead of using a button to encourage followers to sign up for a newsletter or to purchase a CSA share, they encourage people to book public farm tours.

Suzie's is selling by showing, not just pushing a message. By inviting interested people out for a day in the fields, they are sharing their story in a real, "organic" way. These farm tours are incredibly popular as family outings. Once a family takes their child out to the farm, picks veggies as a family, and eats some fresh produce, it's easy to sell them a CSA share.

Always come back to this idea of sharing your story and mission, and not simply pushing your message and products. Don't get too caught up in tactics and strategies. We have the luxury of being local, small businesses. Let's use our advantages to maximum potential.

TWITTER TACTICS

Twitter isn't really a cornerstone of social media for farms because it is conversation-based and takes a lot of time to use correctly. Twitter has about 300 million users compared to Facebook's 1.5 billion. Also, Twitter isn't algorithmic like Facebook. Tweets just show in chronological order. So in order to have any real marketing effect, it's necessary to post the same tweet at least three different times a day. This is best done with a scheduling tool.

A FARM ON TWITTER

There are, however, some fantastic farms using Twitter effectively. One such example is Bossy Acres, run by Karla Pankow.

Karla was a sales and marketing professional for 14 years who gave up corporate life in 2010 to start a diversified, certified organic vegetable farm in Northfield, Minnesota. She and her partner sold 90% of their CSA memberships through Twitter in the first two seasons of operation—an incredible feat.

For Karla, emotion-based marketing works twice as well as promotional-based marketing. I agree with her, because I hear this from farmers all the time. Bossy Acres puts relationships first. They're on Facebook, Twitter, and Instagram, driving interaction with customers.

The beauty of Twitter is that it's just like a cocktail party. It's busy and social. It helps you get in the fray and interact. Twitter is fast-moving. There's such a wealth of information and brilliance on Twitter that it can sometimes be mind-blowing.

Twitter has a level of deep human connection. You can broadcast to all of your followers or have direct one-to-one conversations.

One farm tweeted a picture of a stuffed animal that was left at their market stall. Sure enough, a little boy's family got in touch on Twitter and the stuffed toy made its way back home. Anyone who followed the Twitter account could see the conversation and notice the level of customer service.

Twitter can facilitate the building of relationships.

Bossy Acres engages with their CSA members through a special hashtag. Anything tagged with #bossycsa is specifically tailored to their 100 plus followers who are CSA members. This allows them to sort and filter their Twitter feed. It also allows them to ask: "So #bossycsa, what do you think about _____?" People then respond. It's a great way to get market feedback as well as testimonials and reviews from engaged members.

Karla uses her marketing background to be smart about Twitter. She uses the search function to find hashtags and phrases that people are tweeting. It helps to connect more efficiently. For example, she might search "Farming near Minneapolis" and follow the people who are tweeting about farming in her local area. She'll respond to a tweet and start a relationship. It's not about the hard sell. It's more about building community and support for the long haul.

The larger lesson is to be specific about what you do on Twitter. Farmers have a limited amount of time. We're farmers first. We pull long days. So we have to be smart about how we utilize social media platforms.

INSTAGRAM STRATEGY

Instagram has become a haven for the younger crowd. Millennials aren't on Facebook much anymore. Instagram is where to reach some 400 million users.

Instagram is a much simpler platform, but that doesn't mean there isn't a lot to learn. The main thing to focus on with Instagram is your photo quality (we'll cover more about photos in Chapter 12). You can do as much work as you want trying to build up your following on Instagram, but without amazing photos that tell your story as the foundation, your following won't be very engaged.

What if you already have your account set up and some great photos to share? It's time to build your following. Before we get into the nitty-gritty on how to do that, let's understand how Instagram works:

- **#hashtags:** A way to organize photos by associating them with other photos with the same tag.
- **@mention:** Similar to Facebook. It's a way to call out a user by name.
- **Liking:** Double-tapping any photograph will tell a user you liked their photo.
- **Commenting:** Express something about a user's photo.
- **Tagging:** This is a way to associate a user with a photo. By tapping a tagged photo, a list of users will show up.

That's *all* you can do on Instagram, but it's more than enough for our purposes. The real power comes in combining these actions and targeting the right people at the right time.

Note: While Instagram recently allowed advertising on the platform, it's not the best way to build your following.

To build a following, the first thing you need to do is look at other Instagram accounts. This can be other farms in the area, green living blogs, gardening accounts—the list is endless.

Once you have a list of these, you can start to look at the people who follow these accounts. *These people are your target market on Instagram!* They have already indicated that they like to see pictures that have to do with farming, gardening, and food, so these are the perfect people to target.

Start to follow these people, like their photos, and genuinely comment on ones that you enjoy. While this can be a time-consuming process, you can hire some help or have a family member assist you. This manual process is one of the best ways to build an engaged following from scratch in a very short period of time.

A FarmFan member, Kate Reichard Ramoth, has this to say about Instagram:

> "In terms of actual response, we seem to get more responses/farm visits when we promote specific events, such as a tomatillo sale! Bonfire this weekend! As opposed to just random farm photos. Though people do seem to like random farm photos judging by likes.
>
> Facebook is still a better way for us to communicate with the bulk of our members, but there is definitely a crossover market, and our younger members are

almost exclusively on Instagram and Pinterest instead of Facebook, so I feel like we need to keep up with it to keep everyone connected. During the season we try to post 1 to 2 times per week."

PINTEREST

Pinterest is an interesting platform and can be useful, but the vast majority of small farmers I've worked with haven't had much success with Pinterest as a marketing strategy.

For those who are interested, however, here are a few things to know about it:

With 100 million active users, Pinterest is a highly visual platform that allows you to categorize images into boards, almost like a digital collage board. These boards are usually focused around a particular theme, like organic gardening or vegetable recipes.

It's best to plan out how you want your boards to be structured. I recommend naming your account after your farm or market and creating boards based on specific themes.

Some examples:
- CSA Boxes
- Recipes
- On the Farm
- Market Moments
- Events

Each of these boards will contain all of the pins that pertain to that category. Every single board has a cover image that is

typically the last photo pinned to the board, but you can customize them. Here's a good example of a clean, professional-looking Pinterest profile layout.

All of the boards are themed and have a consistent, clean-looking cover. This helps quite a bit when people search on Pinterest. Well-named boards grab attention. You want your boards to be noticeable, so prospective fans and customers click on them and become followers of your profile.

It's considered bad etiquette to only pin things that have to do with your business. The best approach is to make Pinterest a part of your online workflow by pinning images from other farms and websites that fit in with the theme of your boards. Of course this doesn't mean that you shouldn't post from your own website. It just means that you need to keep a healthy balance.

The real benefit of Pinterest comes from pinning images that get shared a lot and link to your website. This is how traffic flows from Pinterest to your site, and ultimately how you capture a prospective customer's email or phone number.

As already noted, Pinterest hasn't proven to be a great marketing strategy for farmers. If you choose to use it, however, you need to use it consistently.

PAID SOCIAL ADVERTISING

Now that we've covered the free uses of these social platforms, let's take a second to look into what I believe is the only viable option for *paid* social advertising: Facebook. This may change, but at the time of publication in 2016, Facebook ads are a farm's best bet for paid social advertising online.

FACEBOOK ADS

Among other things, what advertising allows you to do on Facebook is make sure that people who like your page will see your post. Facebook ads can also help build a new audience of people who haven't yet liked your page. Ads can help target the demographics and locations you want to reach with your posts.

Facebook advertising can be quite powerful in the right hands, but you have to watch it closely. You want to make sure you understand exactly what you want to get out of advertising. It's very easy to go into Facebook ads and spend $1,000, and still get no returns. However, by taking it slow, knowing your goals, and watching how people engage with your advertising, you can turn Facebook ads into an extremely effective and inexpensive marketing tactic.

Facebook advertising can target potential customers by interest, such as organic food, or by location. You can create an advertisement with a photo and test how different ad copy works with the photo.

Facebook ads provide an opportunity to link people to your site and let them buy at your site. You can even provide a discount coupon code. You can start your ad budget at $5 a day and see how it works. Try changing your ads often to see what works best.

BOOSTING POSTS

Facebook will also give you the option to "boost" a post that has already been posted to your page. What you are doing here is paying Facebook to show your post to more people than would normally see it.

With boosted posts you have almost the same targeting options as with regular Facebook ads. You can choose to target people who already like your page but may not have seen your post. Or you can reach out beyond and target people in your area by location and interests.

Boosting is a good option if you have a page with lots of likes and an active, engaged fan base. It's simple. All you do is spend a minimum of $2 to promote a post on your wall to your audience. I like to use boosted posts to further the reach of a post that's already doing well.

Facebook only shows your posts to between 5% and 10% of your usual audience. If you have 10,000 likes, a post will only be shown to 500 to 1,000 people. But by spending $2 to $5 to boost your post, you can increase its reach by two to five times.

If it's a post that can lead to capturing information from prospective customers and increase sales of your products or CSA shares, it's a no-brainer. But make sure that it's a post that is already engaging part of your audience. The last thing you want to do is boost a post that isn't performing well in the first place.

REMARKETING: WEBSITE CUSTOM AUDIENCES

One really interesting opportunity in Facebook advertising is remarketing. Remarketing makes it possible to show ads to people who have visited your website in the last few months. You can use Facebook's Website Custom Audiences to boost your posts to people who have never liked your Facebook page but have visited your website.

Facebook provides a piece of HTML code that keeps a record of visitors to your website. Then you can create an ad that will show only to these highly engaged potential customers when they use Facebook.

Google AdWords offers a similar remarketing strategy.

As far as a return on investment for your marketing dollars, you can't do better than this. Find out more at https://www.facebook.com/business/learn/facebook-ads-website-custom-audiences.

SOCIAL STRATEGY ROADMAP

In keeping with the "keep it simple" mantra, it's best to turn your social media strategy into a process you can execute as efficiently as possible, then get back to the multitude of tasks you have on the farm. Social media sharing should be slotted into the chunk of time you dedicate to all your marketing activities each week.

First, pick one social media platform as your main focus. And if you pick only one, let it be Facebook with 1.5 billion users. At least for now, Facebook offers the best options for reaching your customers.

Most of your effort should be spent understanding and building a community on that platform. Once you've figured it out and systemized it, you can focus on another platform. This way, you'll guarantee great results on one platform instead of spreading yourself too thin, especially when social media isn't the only marketing task you have for the week!

Focusing on one platform doesn't mean you should completely ignore other ones. Pick one or two photos or stories that you want to share each week and schedule them to be posted, tweeted, and pinned. By using the same one or two photos and adapting them to each social platform that you're on, you can save a *lot* of time and still get great results on social media. Here's a sample routine you can use:

- Pick one or two photos to share on social media for the week.
- Crop and size them for all platforms (you can use www.canva.com for this).
- On Facebook, add a short paragraph telling the story behind the photo.
- On Instagram, make sure to add hashtags along with the story.
- On Pinterest, pin it to the relevant board and make sure to link to your site.
- On Twitter, share it as a photo.
- Schedule all of these social messages to go out automatically (you can use www.hootsuite.com for this).

As you've seen, social media can be an extremely powerful tool for reaching your customers and cultivating new ones. Of course social media isn't a silver bullet; it's not going to ensure you reach all of your marketing goals. Customers won't come flocking just because of your great posts and tweets, but social media offers great forums for telling your farm's story and reaching out.

Online platforms are a great way to bring customers to your marketing funnel. Social media is absolutely essential to your integrated marketing strategy.

CHAPTER 7
WEBSITE DESIGN

Do you even need a website for your farm or farmers' market? This is a question I'm often asked. I've thought about it quite a bit. You should too.

For almost everyone, the answer is yes. There are some businesses that can thrive on a social platform alone like Facebook, but if you're driving sales online, it's much smarter to own your platform. A website allows you to do exactly that. If you're doing any kind of email marketing (which you'll learn about in the next chapter), having a website will also make that process much easier.

If you're just starting your business, I've seen many farms get along just fine with a Facebook page. What inevitably ends up happening, however, is they'll invest in a website sooner or later. It's where people are going to go to see if you're serious or not. When they hear about your farm or market from a friend, they're going to type your name in Google and see what comes up. If your website isn't the first thing that shows up, you're leaving a lot on the table.

Along with the credibility factor, your website is a major portal to explain exactly who you are and what you do. It's also a place for people to make online purchases. It's a site for both marketing and sales.

On your website you can have longer articles about your farming philosophy and why you got into farming. You can introduce your farm staff and family. You can tell visitors where to find you at farmers' markets.

WHAT DO PEOPLE DO WHEN THEY LAND ON YOUR SITE?

Now that we know why having a website is vital, let's dive into the specifics. What do visitors *actually do* when they land on your site? A general rule of thumb is that you have less than a second to capture their attention before they press the back button or open up a new tab to do something else.

Try this experiment: Ask a friend or family member to visit your website. As you look on, observe how they use the site. Ask them to describe what they see, what catches their eye. How do they use the site? Do they scroll down? How are they spending their time? Are they clicking on tabs and links? Do they like the design? Ask them to describe what they like or don't like. What works best for them?

GOALS FOR YOUR WEBSITE

You need to focus a visitor's attention on the one action you want them to take when they land on your site. Do you want them to sign up for your mailing list so you can keep in touch? Maybe sell them on your CSA or products sometime later? Or do you want people to like you on Facebook so they can connect with your farm photos and updates?

Make sure you have a crystal-clear picture of exactly what you're asking of visitors when they land on your site.

- Do you want them to connect with you at a farmers' market?
- Join your CSA?
- Visit the farm?
- Sign up for your e-newsletter?
- Buy products on the website?

Ask yourself, "If I was looking at this site for the first time, what catches my eye? What do they want me to do?"

WHAT ARE THE MOST IMPORTANT ELEMENTS YOUR WEBSITE NEEDS TO HAVE?

As mentioned in Chapter 2, you can purchase a domain name for your website from registrars such as GoDaddy. Ready-made website templates are available from WordPress, and website hosting can be found at HostGator and Bluehost, among others. You don't have to go to all the expense of hiring a dedicated website developer or guru.

If you're already using email through Google, you can set up a blog through your Gmail account.

And as I mentioned earlier, my company Small Farm Central offers a site builder tool developed specifically for farmers. We offer customizable templates, hosting, and tech support tailored to the particular needs of small farms and local farmers at www. smallfarmcentral.com.

DESIGN

It's not enough to just have a site. You must have the right elements in place, and one of the first ones to consider is design. It's not the end all, be all of important elements, but what you're implicitly saying with the design of your site is, "This is the attention to detail that I give to my farm as well." By taking the time to have clear text and properly spaced design elements that help visitors find exactly what they want, you're signaling that you run a quality business. If you put that kind of detail into your site, then you're probably selling the highest-quality produce as well.

CALLS TO ACTION

Aside from design, having a clear and specific action that a visitor can take is absolutely essential. Too many times I see farm websites with nothing to do on their homepage. There's nothing that they want a visitor to actually accomplish. The opposite side of this problem is asking a visitor to do too much: Like us on Facebook, sign up for our email list, *and* make a purchase all on the same page. Making sure that each page is guiding a visitor to one action only.

ABOUT THE FARM

Remember: Your story, philosophy, and history are your assets. They set you apart from fellow farmers, as well as other competitors, like grocery stores. Having a page on the history of your farm and what draws you and the people that work on your farm to the work is important. Make sure that your passion and love for the work shine through on this page.

Add a staff page so visitors can see the names and faces of the people who are growing, processing, and delivering their food and connect to them on an emotional level.

A lot of farms tend to remain rather faceless on their websites, which is a big mistake because the personal nature of your relationship is one of the biggest assets you have as a small-scale farmer. You want new visitors to your farm or market to recognize the names and faces of your people, even if a visitor has never met them before.

ALLOW PEOPLE TO PURCHASE FROM YOUR WEBSITE

If you have a CSA, your site is one of the main ways that customers will purchase shares. Having an online signup process is crucial, because you want to capture people right at the moment when they're thinking of your farm and considering becoming a CSA member. If they have to wait to come to market and sign up in person, or if the signup flow is clunky and out of date, you're losing a lot of money.

A lot of farms I see have websites with CSA options, but they make a potential purchaser print off a membership sheet, write a check, put it in an envelope, and send it off to the farm. This is a big mistake.

People just aren't used to that process anymore. A lot of people don't even have checkbooks these days. If you can be selling things fully online (like your CSA shares), then you should be. Of course, you can have backup methods like print, but the default should be to make it as easy as possible for your customers.

BIGGEST PITFALLS

Now that we have a handle on the essentials your website needs, I want to make sure you avoid some of the biggest pitfalls I see on farm websites. Scan through this list and make sure that you're not making any of these mistakes:

- Having a blog that is really out of date.
- Having no easy way for a visitor to contact the farmer.
- Having broken links on your site. You can use http://www.brokenlinkcheck.com/ to check your site.
- Not having analytics set up on your site (see Chapter 10 for more information).

MAINTAINING A WEBSITE

After you have your site up and running for a while, it's easy to let it go on autopilot and miss out on important information. I encourage everyone we work with to do a yearly review of their website. Even in our own business, we conduct a review every summer. I encourage you to schedule it into the calendar sometime during the winter months, when things are a bit slower.

What you want to do is a website content review. That means you go to your website and you read every single page. Click on your links to make sure they all still work. If they don't, use the broken link tool. The whole idea is to go through everything to make sure that it all still makes sense and is relevant, because things change so often in business.

If you don't do a website review on a yearly basis, pretty soon three years will go by and your website will be completely obsolete. The information is stale and outdated and you'll find your traffic and growth on other platforms has stagnated too. You might have an old CSA signup form link lingering around the site. That just looks flat-out bad. It gives off the signal that you're either not in business anymore, or you are and you don't care very much.

CASE STUDY: THREE SPRINGS FRUIT FARM

Three Springs Fruit Farm's first web presence was a Myspace account, mainly because it was free. But there were disadvantages. There were too many spam bots and fake accounts that didn't reflect well on their business.

As far as sales, Three Springs Fruit Farm got a lot of requests for produce seconds for canning. They used to take the requests over the phone on pen and paper, set aside the order and bring it with them to market, but a lot of times they ended up bringing it back to the farm at the end of the day.

Sometimes people didn't show up to get their order, which meant a lot of wasted time, effort, and product. They essentially lost money too, because they could have sold what wasn't picked up.

Three Springs Fruit Farm needed a web presence that reflected positively on them, and a sales solution that saved time, effort, and product.

Once they invested in a website, they no longer had to worry about spammers and also enjoyed a lot of other features of the site.

As they told me: "We used the blog to talk about our unique growing practices. The produce variety tool was really helpful for answering common customer questions about the differences between two varieties. Our email marketing also grew thanks to the mailing list tool."

Three Springs Fruit Farm professionally differentiated themselves as food producers and had control over all of their content.

Small Farm Central's e-commerce tool made their order system more efficient because people placed the orders themselves. It was also more profitable, because they could ask for payment up front when the order was placed, rather than hoping customers would show up to pick up and pay for their order.

Bottom Line: Small Farm Central's site builder and e-commerce tools helped Three Springs Fruit Farm make their business more profitable and more efficient, and helped it stand out online.

CHAPTER 8
EMAIL MARKETING

E mail marketing is one of the most overlooked marketing channels by farmers and market operators. It's a shame, because it can also be one of the most effective. Email has been around since 1994, but these days it doesn't seem to have the marketing appeal it once did. So many other social channels have sprouted up, especially in the last 5 to 10 years.

However, the fact remains that people are still reading their inboxes. This trend may decrease in the future, especially with younger folks, but for the time being email is still an extremely viable marketing medium.

Connecting with people by email may seem a bit old-fashioned or perhaps too personal, but it's truly a massive opportunity for a farm.

A common concern I hear from farmers is that they feel uncomfortable emailing people marketing messages. They wonder if people are going to be offended or downright mad about cluttering their inboxes. I can tell you from experience that in almost every single case, the answer is "no."

You won't be sending your customers emails every single day. At most, you'll probably email them once a week. If you're providing something interesting, valuable, and relevant in those emails, chances are high they'll be happy to read it. And if they aren't? They'll unsubscribe! That's what the feature is there for.

PLUGGING EMAIL MARKETING INTO YOUR SCHEDULE

Like all of your other marketing efforts, it's important to have a schedule for your email marketing. Sending weekly emails during the season is a good start. You don't have to keep this schedule up in the off-season (once or twice a month is okay), but during the season it's likely that you'll have something valuable for your customers at least once a week. The one caveat here is that if you don't have something they can buy from you at least once a week, you should adjust your frequency.

Weekly emails help build customer loyalty, which we've already determined is a big problem with farmers' markets. Someone might come to you one week and spend $30, but they might not come back next week. You constantly need to keep re-engaging them at a farmers' market. This isn't a problem with CSAs. With a CSA, you sell them once and they're getting their box every week.

If you have a featured crop or vendor for the week, that's what your email should be about. You want it to stoke interest so you get as many bodies out to the market as possible every single week.

OPEN RATES AND CLICK RATES

It's important to use an email software program such as MailChimp to manage your email list. Otherwise email marketing can be a stumbling block, as described in the Common Pitfalls section. Email software programs help you manage the scheduling and timing of emails, which is very important. You can also track statistics. There are two main metrics to watch for: open rates and click rates.

Open rate is the percentage of people who open the email. *Click rate* is the percentage of recipients who clicked on a link in the email.

According to MailChimp, overall industry averages for Agriculture/Food Service are 25% open rates and 3% click rates. You can find the stats at http://mailchimp.com/resources/research/email-marketing-benchmarks/. Local farmers generally have highly engaged customers, so their stats are usually higher. Many of the farmers I work with have open rates from 30% to 40%, which is a good benchmark to strive for.

If you are not getting good open rates, take a look at the way you are using your subject lines. Make sure you are keeping people interested. You may also have a low open rate because the content of your emails may not be as relevant to your customers as it should be. Always make emails uniquely interesting to your customers.

TIMES TO EMAIL

Many email marketing "geeks" have opinions on the best time to email, but from my experience the best approach is simply to test and find out. Just make sure you watch your metrics over time. You should pay attention to your open rate when considering the best time to email.

COMMON PITFALLS

There are several ways you can go wrong with email marketing. Any of them can drastically impact your success. Fortunately, they are all easily avoidable:

NOT USING AN EMAIL SERVICE PROVIDER

Some businesses fail to use an email service provider such as MailChimp or AWeber. Instead they send their emails from their regular email provider. They'll try to BCC their entire list, but accidentally end up CCing or just putting the emails in the "To" field. This means that all of their customers have every other customer's email, which is terrible for privacy. Additionally, if any of your customers has a complaint, it'll make its way to all of your customers instead of directly to you. Such mistakes are easily avoidable with an email service provider.

TOO MUCH CONTENT IN AN EMAIL

One thing I see often are emails that simply have too much information. Every email doesn't need to be a long newsletter. When sending an email, you want people to do or learn one thing. That's it.

Short and digestible is the best approach, especially as more and more people are going through their inboxes on their mobile phones. They're standing in lines at banks or waiting at the doctor's office. Don't send an email that they can't digest quickly. It should be quick and easy to read and look good visually on a small mobile device.

NOT FOLLOWING UP

When people first sign up for your email list, they're thinking of buying a CSA share, getting involved with your farm, coming down to the market next week, or a plethora of other things. Point is, they're highly engaged. They'll open most (if not all) of your emails.

But over time, this engagement drops off naturally and there's not much you can do about it.

To counteract this, you should be emailing them a few times right after they sign up. You can use an auto-responder series of short emails with a welcome series that gives them some immediate value and a reason to care even more about your farm or market.

REDUCING UNSUBSCRIBES: SEGMENT YOUR LISTS

Farmers often attend several farmers' markets and have different selling outlets, including CSAs and farm stands. What is relevant in an email to a farmers' market customer may not be relevant to a CSA customer. Or what is relevant to a shopper at market A may not be appropriate for customers at market B.

To communicate effectively to different audiences, you need to divide or segment your lists according to different customer venues. In this way relevant information and formats reach the right group of customers at the right time.

Segmented lists reduce the number of unsubscribes by keeping email focused on the appropriate people. In this way, you can send extremely interesting, time-sensitive emails to people who want to read them.

And if you need to communicate the same relevant information to all of your customers, you can simply use your master list.

CASE STUDY: RANCHO GORDO FARMS

To show you the power of email marketing, I talked to a great marketer who isn't technically a farmer or farmers' market manager anymore, but he's still a seller. His name is Steve Sando from Rancho Gordo. They sell heirloom beans through their website and two specialty stores. At one time Steve also sold at the Ferry Plaza Farmers' Market in San Francisco, a huge market that enjoys a massive amount of foot traffic. He no longer grows beans himself, but contracts with larger-scale growers to produce his special varieties.

If you have not tried Rancho Gordo beans, you're missing out. Visit the website at www.ranchogordo.com. They grow heirloom varieties you'll never see in a store.

Here's my interview with Steve Sando:

Do you do email marketing?
Yes. We were up to 3,000 people a while ago and now we're at 30,000, which is huge. We know almost to the dollar how much we'll make when we email out to our subscribers now. Within each email, I typically list recipes that link to the bean or product within the recipe itself. That's how we sell.

What content do you put in your email newsletter?
It's a very chatty newsletter. I travel a lot, so I talk about my travels. We have relationships with restaurants, so I always ask them to write up recipes using our products and then I have a

link back to them and their restaurants. It's really hard getting a recipe out of a chef, so when you do it's like gold because it's sort of validated to the home cook.

Our newsletters are probably too long, if you look at it from the perspective of a marketer. But it's chatty and people seem to like it. Like I said, we're up to 30,000 and it helps quite a bit. You really need to do a balance of hard sell, information, outside links, and something personal. If it's all hard sell, people just turn right off. But if you hit the right balance, people will think, "I'm probably going to learn an interesting technique, I'll probably get a good recipe. He's got really pretty pictures from a trip to Italy or something..." You need to provide a lot of value to your newsletter. Only then can you make the hard sell.

Who would you say is your target audience?

My biggest success came when I marketed to myself, because I think I'm my best customer. I think everyone can smell it if you're being insincere. So if it's something you're really passionate about and you really like, I think people pick up on that. But it's nice to know it's probably more a female audience and an old audience, so I probably shouldn't do a lot of Justin Bieber or Kim Kardashian jokes. I might do more Motown references. You have to be careful though, because you can be too cute. But overall, I treat it like I'm marketing to myself. If I wouldn't buy it, or if it's not the way I would want to be presented with something, then I don't do it. It's that simple.

• • •

Like Steve says, keeping your online marketing simple is the best way to *Cultivate Customers.*

CHAPTER 9
TEXT-MESSAGE MARKETING

Text-message marketing is simultaneously one of the most powerful and dangerous tactics you can use to market your local food business. Because of the extremely personal nature of texting, you have an incredible opportunity to connect directly with your fans and customers. But you also have the opportunity to annoy them to no end. It's not enough to simply adapt your email marketing to text. You must re-think the process from the ground up.

I once worked with a farm that had inadvertently set up text messaging with the wrong time zone. Texts that were meant to go out at 9 a.m. instead went out at 3 a.m. and woke customers up from their sleep. That doesn't happen with Facebook updates or emails. The nature of texting is different because it's so immediate. So beware.

One great thing about texting is that people open texts at an extraordinarily high rate. Because most of us are getting texts from friends and family, 90% of people open texts in the first few minutes of receiving them. Now *that* is engagement!

But how does it affect how you should communicate via text?

It means that you need to match the personal nature of texting with the right messaging. Coming across as a company is not the best strategy. You have 160 characters to spend in a text and you must communicate at least three pieces of information:

- Who you are (most people will not have your number saved in their phone)
- Why you are contacting them
- A personal, fun note to humanize the interaction

That's a lot of information to fit into a message that's barely longer than a tweet. However, if you're using a text-message marketing tool, such as FarmFan, you can include a photo. A photo can do most of the heavy lifting as far as communicating these three points. This leaves you room to be fun and personal in the message itself.

HOW TEXT-MESSAGE MARKETING FITS IN YOUR WEEKLY PLAN

Text-message marketing should be used as a last-minute reminder. Think about texting your customers one to two hours before the farmers' market opens.

Remember: Tell people who you are, why they should come, and when they should come.

TEXT-MESSAGE MARKETING TOOLS

There are a few services that provide text-message distribution. Twilio and EZ Texting are a few examples of these services. But you might be wondering how to set text-message marketing up as a system that fits in nicely with the rest of your operation. This is where FarmFan comes into play.

With FarmFan you can segment your texting to the right market (if you sell at multiple locations). We built FarmFan as the perfect solution for farmers to help market themselves. Here's a Q&A with one of our FarmFan users, Karen, from the Lexington Farmers' Market at the University of Kentucky:

What did you think of the texting function of FarmFan?
It was fantastic and I think we were really surprised at people's reaction to it. I think people just liked being a part of something and feeling like it was a special little club. Like, "Yeah I am a FarmFan!" They bought into that idea and they really liked that. People love to show their support for local farmers and I think that really got people.

Of course, the weekly reminder text was great. Our market is every Wednesday afternoon, so when customers get a text message on Wednesday at 11 a.m., it made a huge difference. Folks can plan all week to go to the market, but sometimes life gets in the way. It can be easy to forget. So people told us, "Hey, that was really great, I would have totally forgotten to come if I didn't get a text reminder."

It also gave us a database of contact information to use, which we have struggled with in the past. This was our third year of the market and our first year using FarmFan. The two years before that, we struggled to get a database of people who were interested in the market and who we could communicate with. FarmFan gave us a database of 300-plus people at the end of the season who we knew would be loyal supporters.

Was anyone hesitant to give you a phone number?

Generally people were okay with that. Many were even excited about it. There were a few people that said, "I don't need another text message," but most people were into the idea. Some people don't get text messages on their phones, or they get charged per text, and so they didn't want to join. But for the most part, people are used to texting as a way to do things and weren't bothered at all.

How did you run signups for FarmFan?

They could sign up on our website if they were looking for information online, but most of our signups came from our physical presence at the market.

Was FarmFan useful in converting occasional shoppers into regular shoppers at the market?

Yes. I can probably think of a few people very specifically where that happened—people I knew who were FarmFans but were not frequent market visitors. They ended up coming as a steady routine after I started using FarmFan.

CHAPTER 10

SEARCH ENGINE OPTIMIZATION

S earch Engine Optimization (SEO) involves using keywords in your website pages that match what potential customers are searching. It helps boost visits to your site. When a person does a Google search for local food, local farms, or farmers' markets, it's important that your farm shows up in that search. If you can get your website in front of them at that crucial time, you're most of the way toward gaining a new customer. So SEO is extremely important.

It's also one of the more confusing topics for many people. It's actually less complex than people think, and it's well worth the effort. SEO helps cut through the "noise" and pays great dividends.

You don't need to hire an SEO expert. Far too many farms and markets spend gobs of their hard-earned money on experts, only to get results that they could have achieved for themselves for a fraction of the cost.

You need to focus on two things:

1. **Reputation.** Your website has a "reputation" with Google and there are many factors that go into how Google calculates this reputation. Which other sites link to your site is the most important factor. Links are like votes that say your content is good and not spammy. In short, Google likes links.
2. **Keyword targeting.** You need to target search terms that are important to you and your customers. These are the search terms that, when typed into Google, will display your site in the search results.

Google is always changing its algorithm, which is the formula it uses to determine search results, but that doesn't matter much. The basic formula for SEO hasn't changed all that much in the years since Google was launched.

Google accounts for about 68% of all online searches, so it is by far the major player. However, other search engines like Bing or Yahoo use more or less the same formula for ranking websites. If you optimize for Google, all of the other search engines will follow.

HOW TO MEASURE YOUR SEO PROGRESS

Before we get deeper into SEO, let's talk about how to measure your progress in this area. Without measurement, it's hard to know if what you're doing is working. Adding measurable metrics to your marketing plan ensures you're not wasting the little time you have to spend on marketing and SEO.

While your website traffic isn't the be all, end all metric to measure, it's a good start. Once you are tracking your website traffic, you can compare traffic from one time period to another and see if your SEO efforts are making a difference.

If you're not already tracking your website traffic, the simplest and easiest way to get started is to install Google Analytics. It's the most popular analytics platform and it also happens to be free. Just sign up and put the tracking code on every page of your website. If you're using a platform like WordPress, Squarespace, or any other website builder, they usually have a plug-in you can use to make the install even easier.

HOW TO BUILD LINKS TO YOUR SITE

Now we'll tackle the first of that two-part SEO recipe: reputation.

To build a higher reputation with Google, you're looking for other sites to link to your site. Simple enough, right? But how do you actually get these all-important links?

While getting links happens naturally over time as people talk about you online, there are things that you can do to speed up the process. You can use Google's webmaster tools to see what sites are already linking to your site, if you are curious. It also tells you which search terms were used to find your site, which is very useful in the keyword-targeting phase.

It's important to seed the Internet with links to your site. This is most important if your site is new or hasn't yet established a reputation online. As a farm or a market, there are plenty of opportunities to build online links. Over the last ten years, many local and national directories have been created that list places to find local food.

If your business appears in these listings and directories with links to your website, Google will see that. It does not matter that you technically created the link yourself. All Google sees is a link from an external website pointing to your website.

As you build links, you are also sending real human visitors to your website. Building links is a win-win. You'll get both traffic from Google in the search results and from people on these directories who are looking for local food businesses.

To start you off, there are several national directories you should list yourself in:

- Localharvest: The oldest and most trafficked directory
- Real Time Farms: A crowd-sourced directory for farms and local food
- USDA Markets Directory: For market managers only
- Farmers' Market Online: For market managers only

In my home state of Pennsylvania, we have several statewide directories, such as BuyLocalPA.org and AgMap from Penn State University. In your area, there are likely to be directories like these that you can uncover with a little bit of digging.

To find new directories, look up markets and farms in your area that have a solid online presence. By "reverse engineering" a local food business that's already doing it right, you can take advantage of their hard work.

• • •

KEYWORD TARGETING

The next step is figuring out which search terms are important to your marketing efforts.

First, step back and look at Google's goal. When someone clicks the Search button, Google wants to serve back the most relevant and useful pages for that person. If they can do that, the searcher will come back to Google every single time. Google will make money by serving ads to that person.

So, the question to ask yourself is: For the search terms that I am targeting, what kind of content can I provide that would be interesting and relevant for the searcher?

This is not about tricking Google; this is about working with Google to provide relevant content to the searchers you are interested in.

You should pick two to five search terms to target. This is where the target customer personas you built in Chapter 1 start to be valuable. Ask yourself how the customers you want to target look for a business like yours online.

They might Google terms such as:
• Grassfed beef Pittsburgh
• Farmers market Lexington
• Local farms Albuquerque

Your job is to embed such general "search terms" on your webpages.

Once you've come up with your terms, create pages on your site that speak directly to each term in some way. Put the search terms in the title of the page and a few times in the body of the page. You don't need to overdo it. Google will pick up on the content of your page, so it's in your interest to make the copy sound natural. And you want it to sound great for the humans who are visiting your site!

Now that you've got your keywords and they've been placed on the correct pages, create something of value on those pages.

For example, if you're targeting the search words "Farmers market Lexington," create a page on your site called "Farmers Markets in the Lexington Area" and list *all of the markets in the area*, along with your own. That sort of quality content should win out over time with Google because you're providing a good, relevant experience for their users, instead of blindly promoting your own business.

If you manage a farmers' market, you'll probably want your site to rank well when someone searches for one of your vendor farmers. For that reason, you should have pages on your site that include pertinent information about your vendors. On the flip side, if you are a vendor, you should have a page on your site that names the markets where you sell. In that way, people searching for that market will find your site as well.

CHECKLIST:

1. Figure out which search terms you want your site to rank for.
2. Create content on your website that directly targets those terms.

3. Build links to that content by listing your farm in directories and review sites.
4. Don't think in terms of "tricking" Google. Think about providing a quality experience to Google's users.

Congratulations! You've just saved hundreds or even thousands of dollars by doing your own SEO.

CHAPTER 11
GETTING REVIEWS

When a potential customer is starting to get interested in your farm or market, they'll be doing some research. They'll be looking for one thing in particular: *social proof.* They want to see that other people are already shopping at your farm and having a good experience. They will be looking for online reviews.

Think of reviews as online word of mouth. Many farms see in-person word of mouth as a great way to get more business, but they fail to see the value of online reviews.

In-person word of mouth works very well for people who are just one degree of separation from your regular customers. But if a potential customer doesn't have that personal relationship, they'll look for social proof on sites like Yelp, Google My Business, or Facebook. Online reviews are a way for them to get a picture of what it's like to shop at your farm or market.

Review sites are open forums where customers provide the

content. They are one of the best ways for potential customers to gain a sense of confidence in your business.

Reviews are especially important if potential customers are considering buying a CSA share from your farm. They're going to be spending $400 to $600 and they're making a season-long commitment. They want to understand *exactly* what level of quality, service, and reliability you're going to provide them.

You might be wondering, "Why isn't a testimonial or review section on my website enough?" While you can (and should) feature reviews on your site, from a visitor's perspective these come from a biased source. They rightfully assume that most people are never going to post a negative review on their own website.

Potential customers need an external source to look at, so they're going to want to look at Google reviews, Yelp reviews, or Facebook reviews. These are places where anyone can post anything—good, bad, or neutral. Of course, businesses worry about negative reviews. They worry about the power of one disgruntled customer to leave a negative review and tank their business.

However, the benefit of review sites far outweighs the negative potential. Businesses always have a chance to respond. Negative reviews are something to watch for, but you shouldn't be scared of them.

THE SURPRISING BENEFIT OF NEGATIVE REVIEWS

In fact, negative reviews can paradoxically be *good* for your business. Remember, people are going to review sites to get an honest, unbiased, third-party opinion of your business. When they see bad reviews, they know that the reviews are genuine. The type of person who actively seeks out reviews is much more inquisitive than the average buyer. They are the type of person to read reviews in-depth and evaluate the legitimacy of reviews for themselves.

So don't fret if you have a few negative reviews. Later on in this chapter, we'll discuss how to respond to and deal with even the worst negative reviews.

GETTING STARTED: YELP

There are a lot of review sites out there, but for food businesses, I recommend that you turn to Yelp first. Aside from the power of Yelp reviews, creating or claiming your Yelp page is fantastic for search engine optimization.

Yelp holds such high reputation in Google's eyes that it will almost always show up when someone searches your market or business in Google. With a properly set up Yelp page and your website as well, you effectively have two spots to increase your SEO.

Once you create or claim your Yelp profile, send the link out to five to 10 of your best supporters. Ask them to write a review for you. This way, you're seeding your profile with several reviews from your most enthusiastic customers. Aim to get at least three positive reviews to start your page off well.

EXAMPLE: NORMAN'S FARM MARKET

Norman's Farm Market, a Small Farm Central customer, has a well-structured Yelp page. If you look at the Yelp page, you'll see

★★★★★ 7/23/2014

⊘ 4 check-ins

I have known the Norman brothers since back in my early twenties doing happy hour on Rockville Pike. They have always been hard working - driving from MoCo while in high school to the Eastern Shore at the crack of dawn to purchase corn and turn around and sell it at their original farm stand in Potomac. I bet you didn't know they once had their own market on Bethesda Ave.?

The produce I buy here is always fresh. The best peaches I buy all summer are from this stand. Corn is my close second favorite thing.

Just be cautious when pulling back onto Jones Mill Rd. Come in the afternoon if you can, as opposed to after work.

that they have every bit of information filled out for a potential customer: their hours, address, phone number, and a bunch of pictures. They've done a good job getting reviews from customers as well (*above*).

SETTING UP YOUR "GOOGLE MY BUSINESS" PAGE

Another good page to set up is your "Google My Business" page. These reviews show up in the search results for local businesses like yours. Unlike Yelp, these reviews show up in Google's sidebar search results, as well as their main page. You can now own the top two results for your farm, as well as the entire sidebar on Google.

For instance, do a Google search for Union Square Greenmarket.

As of 2016 when this book was published, Union Square Greenmarket had 75 reviews and some great excerpts that Google provides on the first page. "Love getting my fruits and veggies from this market," is one of them. People do read these reviews. So if you see a "Google My Business" box when you search for your market, make sure you seed these reviews with your best supporters.

There are many other ways to get reviews for your business, including a natural buildup over time. But you should kick-start with reviews by your biggest fans.

FACEBOOK REVIEWS

Facebook reviews are a smaller piece of the review puzzle, but they're worth considering, especially if you interact with customers on Facebook often. They'll show up on any business page you have, and on the main Facebook page for your brand.

Reviews on Facebook are less visible than other platforms because the primary function of Facebook pages is to share images, videos, and posts about your business. But if someone is digging into your business and deciding if they want to go to your market, buy a share from your CSA, or order some of your produce, they'll eventually find your reviews. For situations like these, it's good to have at least a few reviews on Facebook.

Go to your most engaged fans and customers on Facebook and either send them a private message asking for their honest review, or post a request.

LOCAL HARVEST FOOD DIRECTORY

Local Harvest has been around since 2003 and is a massive local food directory, listing over 30,000 family farms and farmers' markets around the country. For a time they were one of the best ways for people to find local food in their area. You can go to their site, type in your ZIP code and the type of local food you're looking for, such as livestock, CSAs, farmers' markets, and you'll get a list of all the places local to you.

As a local food business, your best bet is to create a profile on Local Harvest. While customers can leave reviews on your profile, the bigger benefit is to have a presence on one of the biggest local food directories out there. Its popularity has decreased over the years, but it's still one of the few places that consolidates local food information online.

If you're a CSA, you can create a CSA-specific listing as well, showing where your drop-off locations are to make life easier for your customers.

Getting a few reviews on Local Harvest is a good idea, but don't focus on it as the core of your review strategy. Yelp and Google My Business should still be your main priorities.

GETTING YOUR FIRST BATCH OF REVIEWS

After you've finished creating your review pages, you might notice that they look a bit bare. As already mentioned, you need to seed them with positive reviews. So reach out to the 10 or 20 customers who absolutely love what you do.

When asking for reviews from these people, it's best to make it as personal as possible. These are your biggest fans, the ones who will do the most for you, if only you ask. Send them personal emails with instructions on exactly how to leave a review. Many of them may not be familiar with the reviewing process, so spell it out and make it very easy for them.

You can use a template like this:

> Hi Ken,
>
> Thanks for being an awesome customer!
>
> We are trying to grow our customer base this year and one thing that is really important are online reviews.
>
> We are trying to grow our [Google / Yelp / Facebook / Local Harvest] reviews. Would you be able to take five minutes of your busy day to give us a positive review on [Google / Yelp / Facebook / Local Harvest] that will help other folks find us?
>
> To leave us a review [insert different instructions for different websites]. (Google sample follows):
>
> Go to Google and search [your farm's name].
>
> On the right side of the search results, find where it says "Leave a Review" and click that button.

Give us five stars (hopefully!) and tell others why they should buy from our farm.

Click "Publish" and that's it.

Thanks for your support! This keeps us going year after year!

Your Farm Friends

Try to get three to five positive reviews for each review site you're on. Don't be afraid to follow up with people who haven't responded to your first email. People are busy, and tasks like this often get lost in the shuffle of day-to-day life.

Communicating to your customers how important it is to you to make sure your farm stays around to continue serving them is a very effective strategy. Done well, most people you ask will take five minutes out of their day to give you a good review.

OFFLINE STRATEGIES FOR REVIEWS

Asking for reviews should be baked into your customer service experience, but there are also some practical ideas you can put into place to make accumulating a mass of good reviews easier on you.

Consider creating a flyer that you can give out at your market, market stall, or inside your CSA box. It should say something like, "We thrive on your reviews! Here are three places that you can review us." Beneath that, list your Yelp, Google My Business, and Facebook links. Put a flyer in every bag that leaves your stall on market days.

TURNING A NEGATIVE REVIEW INTO MARKETING

Not too long ago, I had to deal with a negative review. On the Facebook page for my business Small Farm Central, someone left a negative review, but not just any negative review. It was totally ridiculous and erroneous. They weren't even a customer of ours! This person was mad that I'd kicked them out of one of our CSA and farmers' markets Facebook groups because they weren't a farmer or CSA operator. I try to keep those groups very tightly knit so the information shared is as relevant as possible. This person wasn't a farmer and had been giving advice to people who were. It just wasn't a good fit, so I removed him.

He went onto our Facebook page and left a pretty nasty review. At that point in time, we had two to three reviews on the page, so his long, ranting one-star review was very visible. If anyone actually read it, it would've been obvious that he wasn't a customer. It wouldn't have had a big impact on our business. At first, I was upset about it. I found myself wondering how I could get Facebook to delete it.

Then I realized that this was a great opportunity to turn to my customers. I wrote up a post for my Facebook groups for farmers and CSA owners saying, "Hey, we got this negative review. You can check it out here [link]. It has nothing to do with us as a business. However, if Small Farm Central has helped you in any way, I'd love it if you could leave a review that says how we've helped you out."

A day later our page had 29 five-star reviews. Now, I actually like having that one-star review on our page. It's like I mentioned before, if a negative review is absurd and it's the only one you have, it actually functions as a *good* review for your business.

But beyond turning a negative review into an opportunity to garner positive reviews, what can you do as a business owner when someone is less than satisfied with your business? While this isn't a tactic, the absolute best thing you can do when you get negative reviews is use them as an opportunity to dig deep into your customer service.

A heavy focus on customer service is essential when running a local farm that markets directly to buyers. It's one of the most powerful assets you have as a smaller local food business.

When you get a negative review, try to reach out directly to that customer by phone or email and dig deeper into their issue. But wait until cooler heads have prevailed. Don't let your temper or frustration get the better of you. By coming to them hat in hand and genuinely asking how to serve them better, you'll often be able to remedy their complaint and get the negative review removed completely.

Another option is to respond to the negative review directly on the review site. You can do this on Yelp, Google My Business, and Facebook as well. By responding, you're publicly addressing the complaint and showing that you're a responsive business owner who cares not only about your own image, but also about the customers who pay your bills.

It's good policy to respond to all negative reviews, no matter how incredible they are. If someone leaves a review that is unwarranted and baseless, you can tactfully respond with the facts. If someone leaves a review with a genuine complaint, you can publicly apologize, rectify the situation, and show everyone that you're committed to adapting based on customer needs.

You can also head off potential negative reviews by adopting this approach when you get complaints. Try to solve problems before they become negative reviews. While you can't make everyone happy, it should be a part of your customer service process to be as open and honest with people as possible.

If a customer brings up a legitimate problem, often the best answer is, "Yeah, we know it's a problem, and thank you for telling us about it. It's something we're working on. This is how we're trying to address it..." and explain further. Of course when all is said and done, the best way to deal with negative reviews is to never get them in the first place.

ACTION PLAN

You should add review sites to your yearly review checklist as well. If you're actively soliciting reviews every year from your best customers, soon you'll build a critical mass of reviews that skyrocket your review sites to the top of search results, both in Google and within the search functions of each review site.

If you've done a yearly survey, pick out the email addresses of customers who had more positive things to say and send them a quick email based on the template above.

CHAPTER 12
PHOTOGRAPHY AND MEDIA

It might seem odd to devote an entire chapter to photography. But the photos, videos, and media that you promote permeate nearly every single marketing decision you make. Every online marketing strategy is improved by a deeper understanding of images that work.

In working with hundreds of small farms and local food businesses, I've noticed huge differences in the way visual assets are used. Businesses that take it seriously and strive to present their message and story in the most visually pleasing ways have a massive advantage.

Local food businesses typically don't compete on price or convenience. What they compete on is authenticity. What better way to display the raw authenticity of your business than with the best visuals possible?

You have the product that people want to buy. They want to support local farms. They want to see a vibrant local food economy, so it's a necessity to tell the story to capture those customers. The key way to tell a story online is through photos.

ONE PICTURE, ONE PARAGRAPH

As the old saying goes, "A picture is worth a thousand words."

In the current mobile environment, your average customer is multitasking. They're flipping emails and text messages and not concentrating too much on any individual post. They're not sitting down to read a long post on how you moved the cows to a new pasture that day.

The one picture, one paragraph model is more or less ideal content on a weekly basis. A single photograph can depict your latest harvest or a brimming CSA box. You can couple it with 200 descriptive words or updates of happenings on the farm or where you'll be selling next weekend.

EXAMPLE: BOSSY ACRES WOLF SIGHTING

Bossy Acres posted this picture and caption (*right*) to their Facebook account and got a lot of engagement. It's short and to the point, following the one picture, one paragraph rule.

People just don't have a lot of time or attention for reading posts. There are many things competing for their time. But they do want to hear about what's happening on your farm. They want to connect to what's going on. Meet them halfway in a format that makes sense.

MAKE IT EASY TO TAKE PHOTOS

It's so easy to start taking photos. The barrier to great photos has

"First wolf sighting this morning. Just 100 yards away
to the west of our sheep and goats. @#$% just got real."

changed now that everyone has a smartphone in their pocket. I
used to recommend that people buy a cheap camera on Amazon
and keep a couple of them around the farm, but smartphones
are so much easier.

If you do decide to pick up a few cameras, put one in the pack-
ing shed, one in the farm truck. Let your employees know that
whenever they want to take a picture they should. They can snap
a few pictures of interesting things.

Make sure you and your team are taking photos month after
month, year after year. This ensures that when you're struggling
to find something to post, you have an archive of photos to lean
on. You can look through the backlog and find a good story to tell.

TYPES OF PHOTOS THAT WORK

The types of photos that work for farms, CSAs, or farmers' markets will differ. Your unique customer base will engage with different types of photos, but there are some general rules to follow.

Any photos of on-farm work, or "behind the scenes" shots are compelling. This could be the first harvest of tomatoes, tilling the fields, or a new piece of equipment. Remember, you're selling your story. Make your story visible to your customer. Show them!

Whenever possible, include people in your photos. Tell the story of the people who work on the farm and care for the food that your customers are buying. It's a story that the larger chains, delivery services, and food companies just can't tell. No one wants to hear the story of how their factory-farmed eggs are produced.

When people are buying local food, one thing that they hope they're supporting is fair labor practices. It's important to them that people are getting paid well for what they do. Show them how your farm works.

Pictures of children enjoying the farm also work very well. People relate to feeding their kids the best food. Seeing a child enjoying the farm goes a long way. Be sure to always get permission to use pictures of children who aren't your own, or of visitors to your farm.

Animal photos always do well. If you have a farm dog or any other animals on the farm, these should be a staple for you.

One of my favorite farms to follow on social media is Yeehaw
Farm. They've taken the idea of telling animal stories to the next
level. Almost every post on their Facebook page follows some of
their animals through their daily lives. Lately, it's been about the
birthing of new lambs, with cute little captions and stories to
endear their fans. It works well. Almost every picture they post
has hundreds of likes and dozens of shares. There's no doubt
they know exactly what they're doing when it comes to sharing
compelling photographs.

Another Yeehaw Farms story I loved was about the farmer's dad
and a chicken. The photo pictures an elderly man sleeping on
a couch with a chicken at his feet. The story behind the photo
explains how the chicken would scratch at the door every morning to be let in. The farmer would open the door and the chicken
would feed while the farmer's dad slept on the couch. When the

chicken was ready to go out, it would scratch at the door again, and the dad would get up and let it out.

It's a great story about family, farm work, animals, and authenticity. It really brought everything together. It got over 1,000 likes, hundreds of comments, and hundreds of shares. Photography is what brings it together.

BRINGING IN A PROFESSIONAL

Everything we've talked about so far revolves around you taking your own photos, but there's another option. You can bring in a professional photographer to get a few nice photos to use for your website or marketing. While you can take the social photos, sometimes it's a good idea to go to a professional for photos that you'll be using for a long time.

Finding a friend that can give you a good rate is usually the best option here, because photographers tend to be expensive. Another great option is to ask your email list or social following if anyone has a photography background. You can trade them for produce. It's a fantastic way to deepen the connection with your customers and save money as well.

DELEGATING PHOTOS TO A HELPER

You can probably take pretty good photos on your own, but if you're finding it hard to make the time, or feel like you just don't have "the eye," assign someone else to the task. Handing over the photography to a younger employee is a great way to engage them in the farm process. You can even hire an intern who is willing to trade their photography and social media skills to learn more about working on a farm.

The general idea here is that someone who has fun taking photos is going to do a lot better with it than someone who's not having fun, so figure out who that is and give them a daily or weekly task to come up with a nice photo or two.

MEASURING THE SUCCESS OF YOUR PHOTOS

Once you're taking photos and posting them on a regular basis, it's a good idea to see which ones are performing best. Checking your Twitter analytics and Facebook post stats is a great and simple way to start.

Twitter has a built-in analytics system you can find at http:// analytics.twitter.com. You'll be able to see just about anything you could ever want to know about your Twitter profile, but I recommend focusing on these metrics:

- Top tweet of the month
- Total tweet impressions

Knowing these two metrics will tell you which photos performed best, as well as your overall reach on Twitter. Once you know these, you can start to make educated guesses about why a particular photo did well. You can take similar photos in the future.

On Facebook, the best way to measure the success of a photo is by simply checking likes, shares, and overall reach. Facebook works a bit differently than Twitter. Facebook shows your posts to only a small percentage of the people who like your page. However, if your photos are shared and liked by a lot of people, they'll increase that percentage. This is why taking great photos and pairing them with compelling stories works so well on Facebook.

After you measure your performance on these platforms for a while, you should be able to confidently answer these questions:

- What was my top Facebook update over the last month, and why?
- What do the top 10 or 20 best performing photos and stories have in common?
- What gets people really engaged?
- How can I do more of this?

These are questions you'll be able to answer better and better over time. It is a process of continually learning what works and what doesn't.

WORKING YOUR PHOTOS INTO MARKETING

You know which photos work well and you know where to post them. Be sure to work them into your weekly marketing schedule. My recommendation is to pick a photo that tells a fantastic story and write a paragraph of text about it. If you don't have a good photo for the week, go into your photo archive and pull something from the past.

Make it part of a Facebook update and a tweet. On Twitter you can share a photo multiple times over the course of a week. People don't see everything right away on Twitter.

That photo and story can also become a short blog entry. It can be sent in a weekly email. Repurposing compelling content saves time and energy. It's easier than creating a custom piece for each channel. Plug it into your marketing process. Your photos become the face of your communications strategy on a week-to-week basis.

During marketing season a weekly schedule works best. In the off-season, you'll want to keep reminding people that you're still around, but not as often. It's just not as necessary. Once or twice a month is enough to communicate what you're doing in the off-season. The type of photo also changes. You have the opportunity to show what happens when the seasons ends, all of the work you do to prepare for the upcoming season.

PART 3:
SELLING YOUR WARES

🍃🍃🍃

CHAPTER 13

FARMERS' MARKETS

Farmers' markets are competitive marketplaces. You sell to someone one week and then you have to earn their business back the next week. Every week it starts over, which is the biggest challenge. There's no inherent customer loyalty built into the farmers' market model. You have to build it yourself.

If you're a farmers' market operator, there are usually two to three other markets in the area that vendors attend. If you're a vendor, your stall is just a stone's throw away from a direct competitor. Farmers' markets are only open part of the year, a day or two a week, and for limited hours, which adds to the challenge.

In Part 2 of this book you learned how to build customer loyalty into the farmers' market model. Now we'll take a deeper look into how to build your farmers' market clientele.

BUILDING AND CAPTURING AN AUDIENCE

You've seen how email is great for long-term communication, and how texting is great for last-minute messages to bring people to market.

Your customers can and should be interacting with you on social media. But given the choice between social media and direct contact, direct contact always wins. As a direct line of communication, email works well in the farmers' market model.

GROWING YOUR EMAIL LIST

In Chapter 8, you saw how email marketing services like MailChimp provide effective tools to manage your email list. You can also build your list with old-fashioned pen and paper at the market. Always remember to segment your lists. If you work different markets every week, keep separate email signup sheets for each one. In this way you'll know exactly who attends each market and you'll target your messages better.

Emails tend to get opened in the first 8 to 24 hours of receipt. As noted in Chapter 8, customers open about 30% to 40% of emails sent by the farmers I work for. When it comes to marketing, these percentages are very good.

What does this mean for your messaging? It means you need to pay serious attention to the time you send emails. "Come on down to the market" emails are best sent the day before you attend a market.

TEXT MESSAGES FOR THE MARKET

While you're collecting emails at the market, collect names and phone numbers too. You want to incentivize your loyalty and membership programs. You want to make personal connections and encourage customers to keep in touch.

TEXT MESSAGES FOR FARMERS MARKET SALES, A SURVEY

We surveyed over 800 farmers market customers who got text message reminders with the FarmFan app to see how the messages changed their shopping behavior. This is what we learned!

Please tell us how text message reminders influenced you coming to market?

88%
OF CUSTOMERS

I relied on the text messages reminders.

7%
OF CUSTOMERS

I have the farmers market in my calendar and didn't need the text message reminder.

6%
OF CUSTOMERS

I received the text messages by did not attend the farmers market.

CUSTOMERS
SAY

"I especially appreciated the "now in season" texts. They made me immediately hungry for that fruit/vegetable, so I had to stop in. :)"

How do you get information about the market?

TEXT MESSAGE REMINDERS	92%
FACEBOOK	37%
EMAIL	24%
WEBSITE	10%
TWITTER	2%

NINETY TWO PERCENT OF CUSTOMERS **USE TEXTS** FOR MARKET INFO

Would you like us to offer text message reminders in the future?

93% 7%
YES   NO

CUSTOMERS SAY

"I love the text messages. Because of my busy life I sometimes forget to go to the Farmers Market. The reminders are great for reminding me to go! Thanks so much!"

How important were text message reminders in reminding you to visit and buy from the market?

3%	16%	81%
NOT IMPORTANT	SOMEWHAT IMPORTANT	VERY IMPORTANT

A cell number is your ticket to text-message marketing. However, text messages require a different approach than email. Text messages are more last minute than email.

As mentioned in Chapter 9, open rates on texts can reach over 90% in the first three minutes of sending. In a survey of farmers' market customers who receive text-message reminders through our FarmFan app, some 93% said they appreciate the reminders. Texting is an extremely personal medium. Using text messaging in combination with email can be a powerful one-two punch to encourage market attendance.

TEXTING ETIQUETTE

Because of the personal nature of texts, you have to make sure you follow the rules. It's very easy to upset people with text-message marketing if you don't craft your messages carefully.

You have 160 characters to spend in a text. But you may have multiple pieces of information to communicate. So be brief. Let them know who you are upfront. Your phone number is almost certainly not saved in their phone. Introduce yourself: "Hi from Penn Hills Farm." Then go directly to your message and photo.

Imagine this: A photo of a basket of fresh strawberries with the message, "Hi from Three Springs Farm. We have strawberries today. This is the first week of strawberries; we only have 15 quarts! Come down today 10 to 5."

Here's a great one that I received from a market I attend on a weekly basis:

Give people all the information they need, but remember you only have so much time to do it. There's only space to focus on one compelling reason to come to the market. You can't feature all of your produce.

Remember: Tell people who you are, why they should come, and when they should come.

TEXT-MESSAGE SEGMENTATION

As with email, segment your texting to the appropriate market. We provide a segmenting tool with our FarmFan package. Other options for text-message distribution are Twilio and EZ Texting. FarmFan has the advantage of being geared specifically for farms and farmers' markets.

A SAMPLE MARKETING SCHEDULE
LEADING UP TO MARKET DAY

Use a simple promotional system to get people out of their houses and down to the market.

A basic plan would look like this:
* One email 24 hours before
* Social media posts 24 hours before and two hours before
* A text message an hour before

Ideally, these will all be scheduled ahead of time so you don't need to manually send them out as you're gearing up for market.

Chances are good that there's a product you can feature each week. The first week of tomatoes, the first week of melons, or a special variety. Get creative and you'll increase your success with these messages.

GIVE YOUR CUSTOMERS RECIPES

To keep customers engaged and coming back to market, give them a simple recipe they can use. You'll sell more by giving people the tools they need to succeed with their purchase. They'll need to cook what they buy, right?

It's best to focus more on cooking techniques than specific recipes. For example, if you sell greens, you can suggest frying with onions and garlic to wilt the greens for a nice side dish. Recipes are best placed in the emails you send 24 hours before market.

OFFLINE TECHNIQUES FOR FARMERS' MARKETS

Offline techniques are useful as well. When I walk around farmers' markets, it seems that only half of the stalls seem to care if they get business at all. I see people on their phones, or sitting way in the back looking disinterested, or discouraged. For the average farmers' market visitor, none of that encourages sales.

Good attitude and friendly demeanor will go a long way toward bringing customers to your stall. So will good signage.

Your signage display should answer as many questions as possible. You don't want potential customers wandering off to where it's easier to buy.

So, at the very least, your signage should answer these questions:
* Who are you?
* How much does each product cost?

Credit card sales will also increase business. Few people are in the habit of carrying cash. You'll increase your market-day sales with a Square card reader or other major card reader to process credit card payments. Your average sale amount and number of sales will go up. People tend to spend more on credit cards. You'll be paying about 3% on every transaction, but increased sales makes it worth the extra cost.

COMBATING THE POST-SUMMER SLUMP

One trend I've seen is what I call the post-summer slump. It seems that once the kids go back to school, market sales really drop off. People enter a different mode. It becomes even more important to make direct contact with your customers. There aren't as many new products in the fall. It's the old, "Now we have potatoes and we're just going to have potatoes."

Last fall I ran a survey in my Farmers' Market Marketers Facebook group asking, "Do you notice that market sales drop after the kids go back to school?"

The results: 15.8% answered "No" and 84.2% answered "Yes."

This note from a group member summed up the response: "We have found that people tend to assume that the market closes when school starts or soon thereafter. Our best strategy has been to keep telling people that we are open and keep repeating our closing date. Also to keep putting postings on our website and Facebook page about what we have and what is going on at the market so people get the message that we are still going strong."

Another member had a completely different take on the season: "We have greater attendance once school is back in. Families are back in town and University of Florida students are back."

As a farmers' market vendor it's important to know the different seasonal rhythms of the markets where you sell. When you understand the local ebb and flow of customers, you can plan your marketing efforts according to the season. If customer traffic does slack off in the fall you can redouble your marketing efforts to help bring people out.

You'll need to be emailing, Facebook posting, and text messaging to make sure people remember to come!

TACTICS TO INCREASE FALL FOOT TRAFFIC

* Feature one item each week to keep excitement high, even if it is simply a different tomato variety.
* Host special events like tomato tastings or fall festivals.
* Share new and interesting ideas and techniques for cooking with fall vegetables.
* Provide instructions for canning, fermenting, and freezing to encourage bulk buying.

If you can't completely overcome this sales drop with marketing, you may want to plan for smaller harvests and less staff at the market in the fall.

PARTNERING WITH LOCAL MEDIA

A more advanced offline technique is to build relationships with local media and start getting regular press for your market or your farm. I reached out to a friend of mine, Katie Lazor, for her experience in partnering with local media. She's used local media partnerships to grow the success of her farmers' market in a big way.

Katie is the marketing manager at the *Boulder County Farmers' Markets* that runs markets in Boulder and Longmont, Colorado. These are well-attended markets. The Saturday Boulder County Farmers' Markets is known as one of the best in the country. While I was working for a peach farmer in Palisade, Colorado, in 2005 to 2006, I sold at the market. You've never seen peaches move so fast! Palisade peaches are famous throughout Colorado.

Katie's ideas on how to leverage local media for farmers' market marketing is easily replicated by farms across the country. She has a weekly column in a food section of two local papers that highlights local produce and what's going on at the market. This is a mutually beneficial relationship between the newspaper and the farmers' market, as Katie explains in the following interview:

Can you tell me about the weekly column you write for the Boulder Daily Camera?

The idea had come into being right before I got here in the summer of 2014. *The Boulder Daily Camera* and the *Longmont Times Call* are sister publications, and the food editor for those publications is a very big supporter of the farmers' market. She has always been looking for content from the farmers' market as most people see their local farmers' market as a great resource, and an organization that is up-to-date on what is in season, and has good connections with the farmers.

Because of this, we already had a good relationship with these publications as an organization. They were interested in a potential week-to-week relationship. When I came into my position I got her on the phone and we talked about her needs and my needs in this relationship. Then we worked out a template for the weekly column.

So every week we agreed to highlight local produce. This started last May or June, so we were in season for a lot of local produce and we were highlighting what was going to be at the market that coming week. In our paper, the food section comes out on Wednesday. So every Wednesday my column would highlight the season, what they could expect at the market, and one specific produce item.

Say I featured strawberries. I'd give a little bit of information about local strawberries, how you can use them, what growers have them. My favorite part was working with growers. I would find out who was growing strawberries and reach out to a couple different producers. I would share some of their tips or information about growing strawberries or why they grow them or something they love about them. Some insight from the growers, which I think people resonate with a lot.

Then I would reach out to a local chef in our area and get a recipe that highlights that produce. We have a pretty good food community here in Denver and Boulder with great restaurants and really energetic chefs who are starting to think more seasonally. So highlighting what they are doing for local agriculture is important as well. Every week we have a recipe from a local chef in there and that is pretty fun to work with. That outlines the column pretty well. That is how I plan it out and write it out, so every week it is pretty similar, just focusing on a different local item.

How much time does this take on a weekly basis?

When the market is going it takes a little less time because I am at the market anyway and I have a much better pulse of what is going on. In the winter, I decided to do a winter locavore series, basically highlighting different things like local cheese, beef, pork, wine, and kombucha, things like that. Things that don't get a lot of attention during the growing season. These are a little bit more time consuming because I have to do outreach outside of the market and a lot more research into those products. When the market is out of season it is easy to feel a little bit out of touch with what is going on.

Each week I spend probably four to five hours on the column.

Is it a worthwhile investment?

I definitely feel that it is. The thing that I feel strongest about is teaching people what is in season every week since it changes so much. Even year over year it changes a little bit. Maybe there are not any peaches because of a frost in Palisade and it is noteworthy to tell people that. People want to hear why there is more or less of something specific, and when they can find it at the market. There is always that person who really wants to get local asparagus for the few weeks it is at the market. I think that it helps people to start thinking seasonally, and I hope it gets people down to the market too.

Was it difficult to pitch this to the newspaper?

It was very easy. They were as eager for it as we were. I think a lot of farmers' markets can really leverage the knowledge they have at their fingertips and the pulse that they have on local agriculture. The food editor at a publication is focused on a broad scheme of things from restaurant openings to events. If they can get a contact, a trustworthy consistent contact who has a really good pulse on what is going on at local farms, that can be a very mutually beneficial relationship.

If doesn't have to be a weekly column. Maybe it is just being a point of contact for questions related to farms and events. For example, our food editor sent me an email: "I am going write a piece about CSAs in a couple of weeks; can you gather the information that I would need from your vendors, and I will fill in the gaps?" Things like that, being responsive and providing helpful information that is going to benefit both of you. You can't go wrong with that.

• • •

Katie sums it up pretty well. Farmers' markets are a gathering place and a hub. It's up to farmers and vendors to use all the tools at their disposal to make farmers' markets profitable.

CHAPTER 14
THE CSA MODEL

T he community-supported agriculture (CSA) model is one of the most economically powerful models for farm viability. It provides a way to sell directly to customers, which has always been a challenge for farmers. Instead of going through middlemen or distributors, you sell directly to the end buyer.

Customers join a CSA and pay their membership fee in the off-season. Then, during the growing season, farmers are focused on delivering their products week after week. It splits up the selling and producing sides of the business, which can be a very attractive benefit to farmers.

Compared to the farmers' market model, where you're selling and marketing every week, it's no surprise that the CSA model is on the rise. If you drop off 30 to 40 boxes of produce to your members, you can gross $1,000 to $1,500 at once. On top of that, you're not worried about inventory loss as you are with farmers' markets.

It's the best of both worlds for the customer and the farm. The customer gains a deeper appreciation and a stronger relationship with the farm. They understand more about the growing climate and what's going on at the farm. They may even be invited out to the farm for events.

The CSA model typically requires more customer service over time, a deeper commitment to listening to your customers, and the drive to study their expectations and desires.

DOWNSIDES OF CSA

One of the downsides of the CSA model is the potential for misunderstandings between member and farmer. If a farmer also sells at the farmers' market, there's always the chance that something sold at the market may not make it to the CSA share.

For example, imagine you're selling tomatoes at the market, but you don't have enough to put into every CSA box. One of your CSA customers attends the market, sees the "better" produce for sale, and gets upset. They're thinking, "Hey, why did I pay ahead of time and not get the best produce that the farm has to offer? What gives?" This is why managing expectations is so important. If you set the expectations of your CSA members correctly, you can avoid most of these headaches before they ever come up.

COMBATING THE BIGGEST DOWNSIDE OF CSAS: CUSTOMER RETENTION

While it's simpler to sell a customer a season's worth of produce in one fell swoop, you'll still need CSA customers to sign back up again next season. This is where your retention rate comes into play. From what I've seen working with thousands of farms across the country, the average retention rate for most farms is about 50%. That's pretty low. It speaks volumes about which farms do well with the CSA model and which farms struggle.

Certainly, some farms are seeing retention rates in the 90% range, so it is possible to have a high retention rate. When I see farms go wrong, it's typically because they focus all of their CSA marketing on getting new people to sign up. While this should obviously be a component of CSA marketing, many farmers do not even consider strategies to retain existing CSA members year after year.

ALWAYS REMEMBER: IT'S MUCH EASIER TO KEEP AN EXISTING CUSTOMER THAN IT IS TO CREATE A NEW ONE. If you can get your retention rate up to around 70%, your CSA will be in a healthy position. You won't have to work as hard to get new members every year. If you're trying to grow your business, a high retention rate makes growing quite a bit easier.

Let's imagine you have 100 members right now and you're shooting for 150. With a 50% retention rate, you'd have to sign up 100 more people for next season. At a more respectable retention rate of 70%, you'd only need to sign up 80 people.

In the previous chapter, we talked a lot about how to win back your farmers' market customers week after week. In the CSA model, you should think about how every interaction with your customers is winning back their business for the *next year*. It might feel like a long way away, but every time you drop off a box, send an email, or communicate with your customers in any way, you are leaving an impression. Best to make sure that it's always a good one.

Here are some tried and true techniques for keeping your retention rate high.

MEASURE YOUR RETENTION

The first step to improving retention is to simply measure it so you can track your progress over the years. Take the time to calculate this. If you use our Small Farm Central Member Assembler software, this report is available for you out of the box.

The overall retention number is not very useful on its own, although it can be used to track progress over the years. What is more useful for your retention going forward is to break that retention percentage down by different subsections of your membership. For example, try tracking retention by pickup location and type of share.

If you have significantly higher retention at one pickup location than another, you can start to extrapolate some theories for why that may happen. Maybe one of your pickup hosts makes the experience extra-wonderful for your members at that location. You can figure out what the successful host does and try to transfer those traits to other pickup hosts. The key here is that these more detailed numbers will give you excellent clues on how to improve your retention.

For more detailed stats on CSA retention, go to http://www.memberassembler.com/hub/csa-report.

FIND OUT WHY PEOPLE AREN'T RENEWING

When people do not sign up again, send them a survey or call them to find out why they didn't renew their CSA share. Many times it is as simple as a move or that the CSA model doesn't work for them. Feedback from a member who leaves for a preventable reason is very useful. You have an opportunity to improve the customer experience.

ON-FARM PICKUP

Another way to increase retention is to have on-farm pickups. For customers who live near the farm this is highly desirable. It establishes deeper connection. On-farm pickup has higher retention percentages than box-drop locations. Of course if customers live in the city, this isn't a viable option.

MAINTAIN HIGH ETHICAL STANDARDS

Paul of Fort Hill Farm sent me this insight:

> "The CSA model requires a high degree of trust between customer and farmer, so make sure you honor this relationship! Never take advantage of the fact that members have prepaid for their box. They should always get the best product from your farm due to the fact that they have prepaid."

Paul also stresses the importance of not overloading CSA members with "weird" vegetables like kohlrabi.

MARKET STYLE SHARES

In all three high-retention CSAs I've studied, the biggest driver of high retention is the "market-style" CSA. This market-style model has a preset share each week, but products are put out in bulk bins at the pickup location. Members pack their own bags.

It provides more choice, better atmosphere, and community building. People meet each other and talk. Relationships are built all around.

A downside to this model is that the pickup location must be staffed. There is also some product shrinkage. However, retention is golden and it may be worth it for you.

Market style pickups can happen on-farm or off-farm, but if the pickup is going to happen at an off-farm location, site selection will likely be much more difficult. You'll need space to spread out the bulk bins for distribution.

MAKE THEM SAY, "THAT'S *MY* FARMER"

Art from Harvest Valley Farm notes that his members refer to him as "my farmer." This personal connection drives retention, so do everything you can to promote a genuine connection with your members.

POST-HARVEST PROCESSING

Make sure your post-harvest processing techniques quickly take field heat out of your produce and follow all post-harvest best practices. Produce that has been processed correctly will last significantly longer in storage and in your member's refrigerator. You never, ever want a customer to throw product away!

MAKE THEM FEEL LIKE PART OF AN ELITE CLUB

Dave from Gorman Farm makes his members feel special by giving them a special area of the farm stand (the farm stand is open to the public as well). Certain products are members-only, so if someone from the general public wants to buy those products, they simply can't! They need to join the CSA next season.

KNOW EVERY CUSTOMER'S FIRST NAME

Know your member's names when they come to pick up each week. Dave from Gorman Farm encourages his staff to know the names of customers. This makes them feel special and valued. Relationships with farm employees keep members coming back year after year. Much better than feeling like a nameless box of local produce.

PLANT SOMETHING EVERY WEEK

Plant something every week through the season to make sure you have something new to put in the box each week. This holds member's attention and keeps them engaged with farm news and produce seasonality.

GET THE RIGHT MEMBERS

Happy members are your best advocates in the community and they stick around year after year. One way to ensure that you have happy members is to get the right people to join your CSA. Describe your comprehensive membership terms on your website to avoid surprises.

SEND A SURVEY EVERY WEEK

Many CSAs do an end-of-season survey, which is very useful. But for specific timely feedback, consider sending a survey out with each weekly email or a couple of times during the season. You will be looking for feedback on a specific box: What items did they like? Was anything rotten? Did they not get an item?

Immediate feedback is a way to fix problems quickly so negativity does not fester. Remember: A key to customer growth is retention.

ENSURE NO PRODUCE IS THROWN AWAY

The worst experience a CSA member can have is to have to throw away rotten produce. It makes them wonder why they joined a CSA. Members expect the highest quality of freshness when they buy directly from the farm.

Make sure you are giving members the products they want and in the right box size. Too much produce will lead to spoilage.

SEND PICKUP REMINDERS

Chris Blanchard from Flying Rutabaga Works notes that at Rock Spring Farm, "We use our email newsletter service to send newsletters at 4 p.m. the day before we deliver our shares. When we started this, our pickup rate surged from 85% to 98%."

FARM EVENTS

Connect your customers to the farm by inviting them out to visit. This is especially important if most members do not pick up at the farm. Some ideas for farm events:

- Invite a musician member to play music.
- Stage a salsa contest.
- Allow members to pick their own flowers and herbs.
- Offer hay rides.

SIGN UP MEMBERS EARLY

Get members to join your next season as soon as possible. This is especially important if you have a large gap in shares as do many seasonal CSAs in northern climates. Offer an early bird discount. For example, $20 off if they sign up by December 1st.

DEALING WITH PROBLEM MEMBERS

CSA members are with you for an entire season, so having a problem member can be a much bigger headache than having an unruly customer at your market stand. Chris Blanchard of Rock Spring Farm has marketed produce through a 200-member year-round CSA, as well as food stores and farmers' markets. He assists farmers, food businesses, and non-profits in the improvement, creation, and implementation of systems to maximize profitability and quality of life. Chris contributed the following sections on dealing with problem CSA members. You can visit his website at www.purplepitchfork.com/. The principles of managing problem CSA members or farmers' market customers are similar:

- Set clear expectations about the goods and services you provide.
- When a problem arises determine the source (customer or farm).
- Do whatever you can reasonably do to solve the problem, but remember that you will never satisfy 100% of your customers all of the time.

Setting clear expectations is by far the most important principle of the three. There are three times when you should be sure to set expectations:

- Before customers purchase a share.
- The first time you deliver a box.
- During the first few weeks of delivery.

Your website should be crystal clear as to what crops you offer, what your delivery schedule is, and where people can pick up their boxes. Spell out the smaller details, like how long pickup locations are open, and what happens when members miss a share.

When one of your customers purchases a share from you, they should get *all* of this information again. And once you start delivering their share, it doesn't hurt to provide the pickup details and policies again.

Finally, in order to set clear expectations for your customers, you have to have a clear understanding yourself of what you can actually provide. If you don't have the skills, equipment, infrastructure, or land to do what you say you're going to do, you've set yourself up to fail your CSA members.

DEALING WITH MEMBERS WHO DON'T PICK UP BOXES

Everyone's busy, so when a member doesn't pick up their box, it doesn't mean that they're disengaging as a customer. Sometimes people just can't get their box. But it's a warning sign.

Some farmers ask their site hosts to call members to remind them to pick up their boxes. This is a good solution if you can do it, but it's not always possible or practical. You can also send out an email newsletter the day *before* you deliver your shares. Farms who do this have reported a 10% to 15% drop in missed share pickups.

Sometimes members won't pick up their box, but will then blame you for not doing more about it. This is where being clear about your policies comes into play. Will your site hosts hold boxes until the next day? Do you offer a "make-up" box? Do you have the ability to deliver an extra box to a different site on a different day of the week? Can members come select some produce at your farmers' market stand? The more flexibility you can integrate into your operation, the more likely you'll have satisfied customers. However, you can also raise member expectations and create new hassle factors and expenses. So be diplomatic and careful in how you resolve issues.

DEALING WITH MEMBERS WHO DON'T MAKE PAYMENTS

The CSA model is simple: People give you money; you give them vegetables.

If people don't give you money, then you don't give them vegetables. It's like members who don't pick up their boxes. Your best practice is to cut the problem off before it starts. Use a payment service or CSA member management service to set up recurring payments.

You'll still have to deal with expired credit cards and other one-off situations, but this system is far better than manually billing people or accepting forms of payment that cannot be automated.

If you've set up payment plans and people don't follow through, send a nice reminder email, requesting that they send money immediately and reply to your email with a confirmation of their plans. If that doesn't work, pick up the phone and make a phone call. It's not fun to call people to ask for money, but you need to get results. And if you can't get your money, stop delivering their produce. Just make sure you notify them first.

DEALING WITH MEMBERS WHO WANT SPECIAL TREATMENT

Sometimes you'll get a member who wants you to do a little extra for them, such as put their box on hold or change their pickup location. Because they're not on the operating side of the business, they often don't understand how challenging this can be for you as a CSA operator.

It's important to establish expectations for special treatment or *no* special treatment at the beginning. If you're using a CSA member management service, it's straightforward to put shares on a vacation hold or change pickup locations permanently or temporarily. If you manage CSA information on your own spreadsheets this is much harder. You'll need bulletproof systems to manage your information and calendared to-do items.

Your CSA members are individuals with unique circumstances and lives, just like you. If you can make a reasonable accommodation for them, you validate their circumstances and make it more likely that they will continue to be members. But if you know you can't accommodate a request, do everything you can to make sure your members understand before they sign up for the season.

DEALING WITH MEMBERS WHO COMPLAIN

When members complain, it can feel like a blow to the gut. You've put your heart and soul into growing and delivering your crops, and rejection really hurts. Unfortunately, in the real world, effort only gets you so far. Members and customers expect results.

When members complain, it's up to you to figure out the source of the complaint, and whether you can, or even should, alleviate it.

If members complain about rotten produce, you need to determine why they have rotten produce: Did you pack rotten produce in their boxes? Do you lack adequate cooling capacity or quality control procedures? Do you need to up your disease-control game? Did their share sit in a hot location for hours before they picked it up? Or did it sit in their hot car for hours before finding its way to their refrigerator? If the problem lies with the customer, you need to provide education. If the problem lies with your farm, then you've got operational changes to make.

If members complain about prices, you've got one of two problems. Either you aren't providing a good value in your share, or you've got the wrong customers. Value is what a bundle of goods and services is worth to a customer. It has little or no relationship to your particular cost of production. It's a function of customer perception. You need customers who value local, organic, family-farmed vegetables, and you need to provide them with a quantity and quality that matches what they expect. No small feat!

If members complain about the variety of products received, you've got to ask yourself why. Having a diversity of produce available for a CSA share requires intensive planning ahead of the production season, and spot-on timing at every stage of production. Individual boxes should be planned at the beginning of the season, and a planting plan created based on the producer's site-specific knowledge. Successful CSAs I've worked with plan to provide 8 to 12 different items in every box. Four varieties of heirloom tomatoes don't count as four items!

If you have other outlets for your produce, such as farmers' markets or restaurant sales, consider diverting product to your CSA program. Your CSA members have already paid for their products, and while your cash flow may take a short-term hit, providing value to CSA members should increase your retention rates, making a contribution to the long-term success of your business.

At Rock Spring Farm, we had occasional success with the production of microgreens to mitigate unexpected crop shortages. In the event of exceptionally late springs, or severe weather events that put crops on hold or resulted in massive losses, we could produce a crop of Persian Cress in greenhouse flats in just ten days. You can diversify your offerings in relatively short order with salad mix, spinach, and fast herbs like cilantro or dill.

PROBLEM MEMBERS OR MEMBER PROBLEMS?

When you provide goods and services in exchange for money, the primary responsibility for setting expectations and fulfilling them lies with you. Think carefully about the language you use on your farm. When it comes to problems: Is it a problem a member has? Or is the problem really the member? The first is within your power to solve; the second isn't.

The best time to deal with member problems is before they happen. You need the skills, infrastructure, equipment, land, labor, and planting plan to fulfill the implicit and explicit promises you make when you sell a CSA share. You need them before you ever put a seed in the ground or offer a share for sale.

HOW TO APPROACH YOUR WEBSITE

If you market through a CSA, there are some specific concerns you must address to give yourself the best chance of converting website visitors into CSA members.

The first thing to remember is that CSA membership is a big purchase for most of your customers. If it's a share that costs $400 to $600 a season, it's definitely not a purchase most people take lightly.

You must be aware that potential customers will visit your site a few times and do a little searching. They need to know that you're a reputable farmer. Having reviews on sites such as Yelp is a good start. Potential customers can look up your farm and see what people think about it. Because of the competition in CSAs these days, people will definitely be shopping around.

When a potential customer visits your site, your goal should not be to sell them a share right away. As mentioned earlier, it's a big purchase, one that requires education and research before it's made. Getting potential members onto your email list, or getting them to engage with you and your farm on social media, can help you begin the education process.

You need to talk about who you are, what your farm is all about, and the type of produce you grow. All of this can be communicated via these marketing channels as well as on your website. If a customer likes what they see, they'll eventually end up buying a share.

MEET THE TEAM

In order to foster a rock-solid farm-to-customer connection, people want to know the faces of who is growing their food. Always include a Meet the Team page on your website. That's the "community" part of community-supported agriculture. It's not so much a community of people who buy from you as it is the connection between an individual and the farm that makes up the community aspect of this model.

Connecting with you and with other members during pickup makes the CSA model incredibly fulfilling for many customers. So make sure and give them a good idea of who is growing their food.

HOW WE GROW

A webpage on your farm's approach to growing is vital. Videos can help here as well. Your customers want to know as much about their fresh food as possible. So give them good information about your farming philosophy and approach. Make it fun.

We talked earlier about how we don't think it's a good idea for farms to write 1,000 to 2,000 word blog posts. This section breaks that rule. The more in-depth you are on your "How We Grow" page, the better. People are making a big decision here and looking at the approach you take to farming. It's a big part of their decision-making.

~~~~~~

SAMPLE BOX LISTS AND PHOTOS

You absolutely need to have sample box lists and photos on your site. An interested customer who loves your approach to farming also wants to know, "What exactly do I get in my CSA box?"

Part of your marketing process each week should include a photo of a box before it goes out. Some farms really get creative here and take this to the next level. Here's an example from an outstanding and very successful CSA called CloudShare Farms (*above*).

A sample box photo is something you can use everywhere, not just on your website. It can go into your weekly newsletter and your social media posts. Have photos of a typical spring box, summer box, and fall box on your website, as well.

INCLUDE RECIPES

Many farms miss out on a huge opportunity to keep their CSA retention and customer satisfaction high by never including recipes in their marketing. Having a little section on your website for recipes can go a long way. Part of it is cooking education, because a lot of people either aren't used to cooking when then join a CSA, or they don't know how to best prepare much of the produce they get in their box. Giving people a sense of how they're supposed to use the "weirder" produce is important.

Even if it's something as simple as, "Hey, if you find yourself with some extra zucchini, you can just fry it up in olive oil with some salt and pepper as a side to your main dish." It's less about providing the step-by-step process to creating a gourmet meal and more about teaching your customers how to be functional in the kitchen. They should know how to prepare everything in their box, if only at a simple level.

The worst thing that can happen to a CSA member is their food wasting away in the fridge. Sometimes this is inevitable due to life situations, but a lot of the time it's because they don't know what the next step is—how to prepare it.

They start thinking, "Why didn't I cook that kohlrabi. I should have figured it out." While that may be true, you should help them figure it out. Food wasting due to a lack of cooking knowledge is a large reason why people don't rejoin CSAs. Recipes are a fantastic way to counteract that.

GAINING VISIBILITY FOR YOUR CSA

MEDIA COVERAGE

CSAs are always an interesting story for local media. In general, local media is looking for a story about something authentic that's happening in town. You just have to give them a story, which is actually getting harder as the local food movement matures. Five or ten years ago, simply *being* a CSA was newsworthy for many local organizations, but these days it's a little different. You have to be more creative.

One great example of a creative local media pitch came from a farm that started growing a new variety of lettuce called Salanova. They pitched this to the *Pittsburgh Post-Gazette* as the seed for the article and it turned into a wonderful piece about so much more than a simple variety of lettuce. It turned into the nuts and bolts of what it takes to be a farmer, someone who experiments and grows new crops. It was interesting to gardeners, foodies, and even the average layperson. It increased foot traffic at the farmers' market and increased CSA signups. If you can pitch stories like that to the media, you're on the right track.

If you want to explore local media as a way to build visibility for your CSA, you need to start by building relationships with journalists and reporters. Don't go straight into the pitch, even if it's an interesting and creative approach. Email back and forth. Figure out what reporter at the paper covers food and go talk with them. They can help you home in on the best angle for your story.

And remember: It has to be a story, not a list of facts. When spring comes around there's often a need for a story about the local CSAs in the area. You can help them gather the information and pitch it to a reporter. This makes their job much easier and all but guarantees you get the coverage you want.

CSA PARTNERSHIPS

As a CSA operator, you have a huge opportunity to partner with local organizations. You're already creating a community with your CSA, and you can leverage local organizations to help you grow your community. After all, you have to have places for your members to pick up their shares, so why not partner with the organizations that are already graciously offering their space? Churches, gyms, offices, civic organizations, the list goes on.

If you can form a relationship with the person in charge of an organization, then you can access their entire community of people. You'll have an advocate within that community saying, "Hey, this farmer is producing great stuff, come check them out." It becomes a vote of confidence in your farm without you having to go out and build these communities from scratch.

Pickup location and time isn't always convenient for everyone. By integrating more local organizations into your pickups, you can better integrate your CSA into people's day-to-day lives and make things easier. They'll stay with you longer.

You can even volunteer to speak at these organizations. Most of them are always looking for engaging speakers who have new perspectives to share. Any civic organization will usually accept a guest speaker. If that organization is also a pickup location for your CSA, it's not uncommon to sign up a large number of their members to your CSA. Setting up speaking gigs is something you should consider in wintertime when the bulk of the work for the season is over.

Lastly, you can offer a coupon code to people who sign up from each organization. Even a limited-time $10-off coupon for people who sign up through a partner organization can convert a few extra customers, which is a big revenue boost for you.

CSA FAIRS

If you don't know what they are, CSA fairs are basically trade shows for CSA farms. All of the local CSAs in the area show up, set up tables, and prospective customers walk around, talk to farmers, and decide if they want to join.

I'm not a huge fan of CSA fairs, but if you have one in your area, you should consider participating. Most people are going to find you via some online channel or word of mouth, but you may pick up a few extra customers from a fair who might not have seen you otherwise.

CSA coalitions are similar to CSA fairs but much better for the CSA operator. They help advocate for CSA farms in their area. Think of them as CSA support groups. If you're curious enough to look into them more, there's one called the FairShare CSA Coalition in the Madison, Wisconsin area.

The CSA model is tried and tested and still one of the best farm-to-customer models going.

CHAPTER 15
RESTAURANTS

Restaurants are an incredible way to sell your products directly. Whether you're selling produce in bulk, or value-added products like jams and sauces, selling to restaurants is hard to beat. They typically purchase in higher volume and stay customers for longer periods of time. This makes restaurants indispensable partners in growing your farm business. But you have to know how to work with them.

The most important thing to keep in mind when dealing with restaurants is how drastically different their needs are from your average CSA member or farmers' market stall customer. For starters, you'll likely have to deliver directly to the restaurant. Due to their tendency to buy in bulk, you also need a strong distribution system in place to make sure you can handle orders at the restaurant scale.

It's crucial to make sure that your communication with restaurants is crystal-clear. Many restaurants have different quality standards, and almost all of them have different price standards than your typical customer.

Remember: As a CSA or local farm operator, you're not competing with a restaurant. Yes, you're both selling food, but you're not competing. This makes partnering with restaurants a triple-win: You open up another channel of revenue for your business, the restaurant gets to show off its support of local farms, and the diners get to eat your amazing produce.

SELLING TO RESTAURANTS FOR THE FIRST TIME

If you've never worked with a restaurant before, it can be a bit daunting to know where to begin. The easiest and simplest approach is to visit the local restaurants in your area and drop off a box of what you're selling, free of charge.

Before you pack up your produce and head out to restaurants, make sure you know the answer to these three questions:

1. What restaurants are you going to visit?
2. What time of day are you going to visit them?
3. Who is the best person to talk to at each restaurant?

THE BEST TYPES OF RESTAURANTS

Try to focus on local, farm-to-table restaurants. It's much harder to sell to a chain restaurant and likely not worth the hassle, even if you do manage to foster a relationship. If a chain restaurant is something you want to explore, you'll usually need proof of working with restaurants successfully in the past. This means you still need to build your first relationships with smaller, more local establishments before you can consider big chains.

It's an easy sell to the farm-to-table type of restaurant. They share the same values as you and likely already work with some farms in your area.

THE BEST TIME TO VISIT A RESTAURANT

When deciding what time to visit a restaurant, keep this rule in mind: Never visit when they are in service. Ever. Not only will you have no chance of speaking to a decision-maker in the kitchen, it will make you look like you don't "speak the language."

The best times to visit are in-between service, typically around 2 to 4 p.m. for most restaurants. During these hours, most chefs are prepping for the next service, but also have some open time where they can take a break and relax. Not only will you have a much higher chance of talking to the buyer for the kitchen, they'll also be in a much better mood during these hours. It's hard work in the kitchen. Recognize and respect this fact and you'll have better results!

WHO TO TALK TO AT A RESTAURANT

Speaking of kitchen decision makers, it's important to understand the hierarchy of a kitchen.

At the top, you have executive chefs. While they make all of the decisions on a large scale, it's best to think of them as the CEO of the kitchen, They aren't someone you go to for every little decision. They have people under them assigned to specific roles. While some executive chefs will make the final call on purchasing product, often times that decision is pushed down the chain.

The *chef de cuisine* is the official chief of the kitchen. This person runs the day-to-day operations, creating new recipes and often making purchasing decisions. If you can speak to the *chef de cuisine*, go for it. This is your best chance at making the sale.

Sometimes you can't get in touch with the *chef de cuisine* and must instead speak to the *sous chefs*. Translated from French, these are the "under-chiefs" of the kitchen and are best thought of as the assistants to the *chef de cuisine*. More often than not, you'll be talking to the *sous chefs*, especially during the hours of 2 to 4 when the *chef de cuisine* is often taking a break.

BEST PRACTICES FOR BRINGING IN YOUR PRODUCE

If you do decide to bring a box of produce, make sure that the *sous chefs* see the quality of your food. Your produce will be more expensive than the substitutes they can get from food distributors, especially if you grow organic. Unless they're committed to farm-to-table food, they're probably used to buying traditionally grown produce. You have to be able to sell them on something more than price, so the quality and flavor of your food, along with your story, are strong angles to take.

When talking to chefs, keep in mind that many are a lot like farmers. They're often very do-it-yourself and prefer doing things in their own way. They work in the back of the house, unseen by the people who actually keep their business alive. There's definite kinship between chefs and farmers, so nurturing that as you approach them will pay off big time.

If you prefer a lower-investment approach to test out restaurants as a sales channel, you can make a list of all of the chefs in your area and send them all an email about your farm and what you have to offer. This can be a good way to gauge interest in your product, but be warned: Many chefs don't work well with email. You might not receive many responses and get discouraged. If you decide to go the email route, be sure to follow up.

Phone calls can be very effective when dealing with chefs, because they're always on their phones and rarely get behind a computer. Just make sure to call during hours when they aren't hard at work preparing dishes.

PROMOTING YOUR BUSINESS WITH RESTAURANTS

Along with selling to restaurants, there are many ways you can co-promote to increase the visibility of your farm and food.

"MEET THE FARMER" HAPPY HOURS

One strategy that works extremely well came from a farm that had a CSA and sold to a few local restaurants. A few times a year, the farmer visited the restaurants and would do a "meet the farmer" happy hour. In addition to regular customers at the restaurant, the farmer would send an email out to his CSA list and invite them all out for the event.

Everyone came out to the bar for a relaxed happy hour. While CSA members got to know each other a bit, it was more important that they got to talk to their farmer. The farmer combined the event with the annual signup for his CSA, which was a great way for his members to commit to another year of fresh produce.

This type of strategy is very easy to pull off, because you're delivering customers directly to the restaurant. No restaurant on

Earth is going to complain about that! On top of that, you get to connect with your CSA members, they get to meet each other, and you'll probably get some of your members to renew their CSA share that may not have otherwise. It's a win all around.

GET YOUR FARM'S NAME ON THE MENU

A simple thing you should be doing if you're selling to restaurants is requesting that the restaurant list you on their menu. Instead of describing a dish as a "Greek salad with arugula and pistachios," diners could be having a "Greek salad with Silverwind Farms arugula and pistachios." It's a very simple way to get some additional exposure for your farm, especially if the dish is popular.

CSA INFORMATION POSTED IN ENTRYWAY

You should ask every restaurant that uses your produce to place some info cards with your CSA details in their entryway. This way, any diners who loved a dish that used your produce have a chance of signing up for your CSA.

CO-PROMOTING ON SOCIAL MEDIA

A final way to boost your visibility is to ask restaurants to share your story, produce, or dishes on their social media accounts. This taps you into the wider market of that restaurant's customers without too much effort.

However, you need to remember: The more you can do to make their lives easier, the better. No one who works at a restaurant has free time to help you out. They're certainly not going to suggest this on their own. If you want to make this happen, do as much as you can for them in advance.

This means giving them the hook, the images, and even the descriptions or copy ready to go. If you're going to ask a restaurant to send an email out to their list about your CSA, you'd better write that email up and send it over to whoever is in control of their email list. They are infinitely more likely to help you out if all they need to do is copy, paste, and click a few buttons.

That's not to say that restaurants are lazy, far from it. This is a principle you should apply to all of your marketing efforts when working with partner organizations. Everyone is busy and everyone has a million and one things to do in their day. Remove as many barriers to action as possible and you'll be much more successful.

CASE STUDY: TREVETT HOOPER FROM LEGUME

I sat down with a good friend of mine, Trevett Hooper, to talk about the farm and restaurant partnership. He runs a well-regarded farm-to-table restaurant in Pittsburgh named Legume. He is an owner-chef. He works with Who Cooks for You Farm, Penn's Corner, and is very serious about working with farms, so his viewpoint might be different than other chefs. He took time out of his busy schedule to answer a few questions:

How can farms engage with new restaurant clients?

Remember, chefs have no time. We're coming up with new menu items, prepping, or in the back actually cooking food for our customers. If you want to get in touch with a chef, a single email won't cut it. You may have to follow up a few times.

If that doesn't work, just show up at the restaurant during slow hours and try to talk to the chef. Perseverance is key here, and we won't be bothered by it.

If you manage to get hold of a chef, seek first to build a relationship on a friend level. Invite them out to the farm on an off day and include extras in the produce that you deliver for them to experiment with. That's the type of relationships that will drive the business over the years.

Do you participate in any cross-promotion opportunities?

One strategy I've used with farms is to use Legume as the drop-off point for their CSA. Restaurant customers who walk in are intrigued by the boxes and sometimes buy a membership for themselves.

I don't put the names of the farms I work with on my menu, but my wait staff is very aware of all the ingredients in each of my dishes and where they came from. The farms I work with get exposure when my wait staff answers customer questions about particular menu items.

What is most important to you as a restaurateur?

Forming long-term relationships with farms is vital to my restaurant. I need these partnerships to get a high volume of quality produce that I can use for preservation purposes. For example, I recently contracted with a grower to deliver 1,000 pounds of paste tomatoes for tomato sauce preservation in the fall. I got these tomatoes far lower than retail price, but it was an agreed upon price that made sense at that volume.

I try to make sure it's a mutually beneficial relationship. Too many chefs want to buy a couple of pounds for garnishes, but at Legume I try to purchase in volume.

What do you expect for pricing?

I don't compare the produce prices that my farmers offer with the wholesale market. The only two questions on my mind are, "How does this item add value to the plate?" and "How much can I charge for this dish?"

How should farms communicate with chefs on an ongoing basis?

I like to get weekly price lists, but often forget to order because things get crazy at the restaurant. The best farmers I work with shoot me a reminder text so I commit to buying that week.

How do you tell your customers about suppliers?

I promote the farms that I work with through our restaurant's blog, email list, and events like "Meet the Farmer Happy Hour" that we run from time to time.

AN EXCELLENT VENUE

Yes, selling to restaurants is hard to beat. If you can tap this market, you'll be cultivating like-minded customers for high-volume sales. When you understand the specific needs of restaurateurs and how to approach them, you'll be scaling up your business for profitability.

CONCLUSION
TIME TO GET CULTIVATING

I sincerely hope that *Cultivating Customers* has demystified the process of marketing your local food business online. While I'm not presently running a farm, I work with hundreds of farmers, farmers' markets, CSAs, and local food businesses to provide the tools they need to succeed.

In these digital times, competition has grown stiff from all quarters. As I mentioned in the introduction, we're at a crossroads where big food companies and startups are competing for local farmers' dollars. The landscape for farm-fresh food has changed dramatically.

Local farms and markets need to mature to compete with food-tech startups, online sellers, and food chains. We need to up our game. By embracing social media and reaching out to customers and potential customers in the digital world, small farms can expand their customer base exponentially.

In *Cultivating Customers,* you've learned how to engage customers with a personal touch both online and in person. You've gained insight into the customer "persona" and the customer "lifecycle." By establishing relationships and connecting on common ground, we are raising interest in local food, fresh ingredients, and eating well.

In these pages you've learned the digital ropes for turning occasional customers into weekly customers. You've seen how central your own story is to connecting to customers, gaining their confidence, and increasing your market share.

You've been introduced to the marketing funnel and the phases of the customer lifecycle. You've learned how to bridge the gap from awareness to engagement to commitment.

Most importantly you've gained an understanding and working knowledge of online marketing strategies and tactics to reach potential customers and build retention. You are better equipped now to use social media, websites, and email to tell your local food story.

With my background in farming and technology, I decided to go into business to help small farmers make money at what they do best. It's why I started Small Farm Central. I wanted to connect professional farmers to digital resources that serve their need for a sustainable living.

To this end I developed the FarmFan app to engage social media such as Facebook and text messaging, along with email lists, websites, and loyalty programs to make digital marketing easier for farmers, farmers' markets, and local food businesses.

As I've said, farmers need to see themselves as "food entrepreneurs" and "agripreneurs." We need to make marketing and promotion central, because farming is a business.

Yes, it's time to take the digital bull by the horns—or be left on the compost heap.

I invite you to visit Small Farm Central online at smallfarmcentral.com, check out our services, and sign up for our free Farm Marketing Minute. Find out more about FarmFan at about.farmfanapp.com, and feel free to contact me at simon@smallfarmcentral.com.

MARKETING PLAN WORKSHEET

Date: _____ **Completed by:** _____

1. My perfect customer is...

2. When customers think about my farm or market, they think....

3. My main ways of finding new customers are (circle all that apply):

Blog   Social media

Word of mouth   Website

Directories   Other:

4. My three Key Performance Indicators (KPIs) are...
(for example: market sales, CSA signups, website visitors, social media following, email signups). Include measurable end-of-year goals for each.

-

-

-

5. My current email list size is _____ email addresses. By the end of next year, I will have _____ email addresses on my list.

6. I pledge to dedicate _____ minutes every week throughout the season to marketing. I will schedule time between _____ and _____ each _____ (day of week) as marketing time to meet this goal.

7. I will take _____ photos at the farm or market per week throughout the season.

8. When a customer comes to my website, I want them to (for example: sign up for mailing list, "like" me on Facebook, buy something):

-

-

-

9. My Search Engine Optimization (SEO) key phrases are... Create one page on your site dedicated to each.

-
-
-
-
-

10. Yearly checklist for reviews:

- Website content review. Look at every page on your website.
- Marketing goals review: Review last year's goals and do this again.
- Farm directories review: Make a goal to add ——————— links (at least 5 to 10) each off-season.

ABOUT
THE AUTHOR

Simon grew up on a small farm in the hills of southwestern Pennsylvania before pursuing a degree in Information Sciences and Technology at Penn State University. In 2006, he founded Small Farm Central to serve the technology needs of farmers. Since then, over 1,000 farms, farmers' markets, fisheries, and other local foods businesses have utilized Small Farm Central's tools.

Simon is also kept active by his two sons, Eliot and Theo. He enjoys food experimentation projects like beer making, fermenting various vegetables, and whatever other challenges come up. The 70-acre farm is still in the family, so there is a chance of returning to growing food some day!

Made in the USA
Middletown, DE
30 May 2017